Macfarlane

W9-CAI-689

ANSWER KEY & TEST BANK

Table of Contents

Algebra 2: A Teaching Textbook™
Answer Key and Test Bank
First Edition

Copyright © 2004 by Teaching Textbooks, Inc.

Printed in the United States of America.

ISBN: 0-9749036-9-8

Teaching Textbooks, Inc.
P. O. Box 60529
Oklahoma City, OK 73146
www.teachingtextbooks.com

CHAPTER 1

Practice 1

a. Expression

b. $3.8x$

c. $\dfrac{x}{4} = 3$

d. $x - 6 = 8$

e. Yes

Problem Set 1

1. True
2. False
3. True
4. C
5. B
6. A
7. E
8. C
9. Algebra
10. Arithmetic
11. Algebra
12. Expression
13. Equation
14. Expression
15. $5.2x$
16. $x + 4$
17. $\dfrac{x}{7}$
18. $x - 21$
19. $x + 15 = 40$
20. $4x = 88$
21. $\dfrac{x}{16} = 2$
22. $x - 10 = 31$
23. $\dfrac{7}{3}$
24. 8
25. $\dfrac{2}{3}$

Practice 2

a. $\dfrac{1}{2}(3 + 4)$

b. $6(2) - 8$

c. $5(x + 3) = 25$

d. $\dfrac{x + 2}{3} = 12$

e. Yes

Problem Set 2

1. True
2. True
3. False
4. False
5. A
6. E
7. C
8. $5x$
9. $\dfrac{y}{2}$
10. 18
11. 26
12. 13
13. 3
14. 16
15. 7
16. $4(3) + 11$
17. $\dfrac{1}{3}(10 + 5)$
18. $8(7 - 5)$
19. $2(3) - 4$
20. $12x - 9 = 37$
21. $2(x + 4) = 20$
22. $\dfrac{x + 8}{2} = 12$
23. $\dfrac{7}{5}$
24. $\dfrac{10}{3}$
25. $\dfrac{6}{5}$

Practice 3

a. $5x - 8 = 42$

b. 5

c. 5

d. 7

e. 3

Problem Set 3

1. True
2. True
3. True
4. A
5. E
6. 0
7. 8
8. 36
9. $\dfrac{7}{8}$
10. $\dfrac{14}{3}$
11. $19 - \dfrac{56}{8}$
12. $\dfrac{8 + 12}{3}$
13. $13(8 - 2)$
14. $3(5) - 9$
15. $\dfrac{x}{3} + 4 = 8$
16. $2x - 6 = 38$
17. $\dfrac{x + 5}{4} = 3$
18. 2
19. 9
20. 24
21. 12
22. 3
23. 8
24. 11
25. 5.5

Practice 4

a. 6

b. 4

c. 7

d. $\dfrac{119}{5}$

e. 8%

Problem Set 4

1. False
2. True
3. 7
4. 3
5. 1
6. 72
7. $\dfrac{9}{5}$
8. $\dfrac{56+42}{11}$
9. $8(4-3)$
10. $10-7\left(\dfrac{1}{2}\right)$
11. $\dfrac{x+9}{2}=8$
12. $\dfrac{x}{6}+4=10$
13. $2.5x-2=3$
14. 10
15. 5
16. 10
17. 16
18. 5
19. 10
20. 9
21. 5
22. $\dfrac{59}{2}$
23. 7.5%

Practice 5

a. -10
b. 21
c. 2
d. 1
e. $2

Problem Set 5

1. False
2. True
3. False
4. D
5. E
6. E
7. $-5,500$
8. -48
9. -8
10. -6
11. -24
12. -24
13. -36
14. 36
15. 2
16. $\dfrac{18-6}{5}$
17. $11\cdot\dfrac{9}{4}$
18. 17
19. 6
20. 6
21. 5
22. 8
23. $\dfrac{22}{5}$
24. 3
25. $4

Practice 6

a. $-\dfrac{5}{8}$
b. Yes.
c. -29
d. -21
e. 60

Problem Set 6

1. False
2. True
3. True
4. -4.7

5. $\dfrac{5}{12}$
6. -14
7. 48
8. $-\dfrac{4}{7}$
9. -3
10. -5
11. 9
12. Yes
13. No
14. No
15. $-2(-7+4)$
16. $-3(5)-18$
17. 8
18. 5
19. 43
20. 15
21. 3
22. 18
23. 27
24. -6

Practice 7

a. $\dfrac{8}{15}$
b. 55
c. -45
d. -20
e. 853 yards

Problem Set 7

1. True
2. False
3. -6
4. 11
5. -238
6. $-\dfrac{2}{3}$
7. -4
8. -3

9. $\dfrac{15}{28}$

10. Yes

11. Yes

12. $\dfrac{-18}{-3} - 4$

13. $\dfrac{7 - 13}{2}$

14. -4

15. -117

16. 7.5

17. 87

18. -5

19. 82

20. -6

21. -16

22. -210

23. -12

24. 30,328 feet

CHAPTER 2

Practice 8
a. No
b. Yes
c. Yes
d. −15
e. $1.75

Problem Set 8
1. True
2. True
3. A
4. B
5. C
6. D
7. −16
8. −181
9. −16.5
10. 5
11. $-\dfrac{1}{4}$
12. −220
13. No
14. Yes
15. Yes
16. Yes
17. −40
18. 1
19. 70
20. 27
21. −28
22. 108
23. −16
24. $2.75

Practice 9
a. Yes
b. Yes
c. No
d. 2
e. −5

Problem Set 9
1. True
2. True
3. 17.5
4. 0
5. 118.75
6. 6
7. $\dfrac{3}{10}$
8. $-\dfrac{1}{3}(21)+14$
9. $\dfrac{-10+(-9)}{-5}$
10. Yes
11. No
12. Yes
13. Yes
14. Yes
15. 2
16. 60
17. 1
18. −91
19. $-\dfrac{1}{9}$
20. −63.2
21. 63
22. 11
23. $-\dfrac{21}{4}$
24. $1.75

Practice 10
a. Yes
b. Yes
c. 14
d. 15
e. 5,000 dresses

Problem Set 10
1. True
2. True
3. True

4. −9
5. −1
6. 0
7. −9
8. 1
9. 16.8
10. Yes
11. Yes
12. Yes
13. No
14. Yes
15. 9
16. 1
17. 9
18. 4
19. −4
20. 49.5
21. 5
22. 1
23. 5
24. 100,000 boxes

Practice 11
a. Yes
b. $\dfrac{5}{6}$
c. −24
d. 9
e. $50

Problem Set 11
1. True
2. False
3. −9
4. $-\dfrac{1}{15}$
5. −36.8
6. −7
7. 1
8. 11
9. Yes
10. No
11. Yes

12. $-8x$
13. $6x+24$
14. $-12x-6$
15. 3
16. 42
17. -27
18. 21
19. 7
20. -14
21. 5
22. 1
23. $45

Practice 12

a. 15
b. Yes
c. $\dfrac{3}{5}x+3$
d. -20
e. $80,000

Problem Set 12

1. True
2. True
3. -8
4. 16
5. 8
6. -25
7. 2
8. 16
9. Yes
10. No
11. Yes
12. $-3x-6$
13. $6.4x$
14. $\dfrac{2}{7}x+2$
15. 7
16. 2
17. -320
18. $\dfrac{5}{3}$
19. 26

20. -5
21. 15
22. -1
23. $300,000

Practice 13

a. $3[3(4+2)-15]$
b. Yes
c. $30x-60$
d. 3
e. 32 patients

Problem Set 13

1. True
2. False
3. True
4. -30
5. 9
6. 3
7. 62
8. 18
9. $2[4(7+1)-8]$
10. $5[3(x+6)-2]$
11. No
12. No
13. Yes
14. $-10x$
15. $-20+5x$
16. $6x-6$
17. 3
18. 2
19. $-\dfrac{5}{2}$
20. -45
21. -135
22. $-\dfrac{1}{2}$
23. 5
24. 360 customers

Practice 14

a. Yes

b. No
c. -8
d. $\dfrac{5}{13}$
e. $24

Problem Set 14

1. True
2. True
3. $-\dfrac{7}{6}$
4. -10
5. 0
6. -16
7. $-7[5-2(7+8)]$
8. $-5[3-4(x+9)]$
9. Yes
10. No
11. No
12. $\dfrac{5}{2}x$
13. $-12-2x$
14. $3x-14$
15. $15x+32$
16. -20
17. -6
18. -46
19. 4
20. $\dfrac{3}{7}$
21. 20
22. -1
23. $20

Practice 15

a. 1
b. -15
c. False equation
d. Identity
e. $7,500

Problem Set 15

1. False
2. True
3. True
4. -32
5. 6
6. 0
7. -57
8. $5\{4[2+(-8)]+6\}$
9. $2\{7[x+(-1)]+3\}$
10. Yes
11. Yes
12. $8.8x$
13. $15-x$
14. $12x+6$
15. $-x$
16. -3
17. $-\dfrac{6}{5}$
18. -5
19. 42
20. False equation
21. Identity
22. $15,000

8. $-2[2(3-8)+5]$
9. $-8[3(x-1)+9]$
10. Yes
11. Yes
12. $7+5x$
13. $\dfrac{1}{2}x-3$
14. $-\dfrac{1}{2}y$
15. $3x-2$
16. $8x-2$
17. $-\dfrac{23}{2}$
18. 3
19. -6
20. -2
21. -6
22. -4
23. 2 hours

Practice 16

a. $x+3$
b. $15x+(-9)$
c. 5
d. $-\dfrac{5}{6}$
e. $\dfrac{1}{2}$ hour

Problem Set 16

1. True
2. False
3. 19
4. -13.5
5. -3
6. 11
7. 4

CHAPTER 3

Practice 17

   a. $20 - \{-3[10 + 4(x - 2)]\}$
   b.   No
   c. $-5x$
   d.   3
   e.   3 seconds

Problem Set 17

1. False
2. True
3. True
4. False
5. -15
6. 27
7. 4
8. -9
9. $23 - \{-9[4 + 5(3 - 2)]\}$
10. $17 - \{-2[8 + 2(x - 3)]\}$
11. Yes
12. No
13. $-5x$
14. $\dfrac{x}{6}$
15. $6x + 4$
16. $-\dfrac{1}{2x}$
17. $\dfrac{5}{2}$
18. $-4x$
19. $\dfrac{5}{8}$
20. 2
21. -3
22. 6
23. 2
24. 3 seconds

Practice 18

   a.   Yes

   b. $\dfrac{3x + 9}{x - 3}$
   c. $\dfrac{1}{3}$
   d. -11
   e.   8 seconds

Problem Set 18

1. True
2. True
3. -2
4. $-\dfrac{3}{10}$
5. -1
6. -2
7. -14
8. No
9. No
10. Yes
11. $-\dfrac{1}{6}$
12. $\dfrac{1}{x - 3}$
13. $\dfrac{4x - 9}{4x}$
14. $-\dfrac{1}{5}$
15. $\dfrac{2x + 4}{x - 2}$
16. $\dfrac{1}{2}$
17. -30
18. 2
19. $\dfrac{6}{5}$
20. -8
21. Identity
22. $\dfrac{3}{2}$
23. 140 seconds

Practice 19

a. Yes

b. $\dfrac{1}{6}$

c. $\dfrac{15x+5}{8x}$

d. $\dfrac{4}{5}$

e. 7.5 pounds

Problem Set 19

1. True
2. True
3. False
4. -16
5. 39
6. -3
7. 0
8. 0
9. Yes
10. Yes
11. No
12. $\dfrac{1}{10}$
13. $\dfrac{1}{8}$
14. $\dfrac{3x}{2-x}$
15. $\dfrac{6x+3}{5x}$
16. $-4x-6$
17. $\dfrac{1}{7}$
18. $\dfrac{5}{9}$
19. 2
20. 33
21. $-\dfrac{24}{5}$
22. 1
23. 15 pounds

Practice 20

a. No

b. $\dfrac{7}{9x}$

c. $\dfrac{9x+11}{2x}$

d. -4

e. 4 milliliters

Problem Set 20

1. True
2. True
3. 12
4. -5
5. -30
6. 4
7. -10
8. No
9. Yes
10. $5x-12$
11. $\dfrac{5}{8x}$
12. $-\dfrac{1}{3}$
13. $\dfrac{5x+1}{3x}$
14. $\dfrac{x+4}{2}$
15. 4
16. 9
17. $-\dfrac{1}{7}$
18. $\dfrac{1}{12}$
19. -28
20. False equation
21. -3
22. 30 milligrams

Practice 21

a. No

b. $\dfrac{1}{27}$

c. $\dfrac{12x}{x+3}$

d. $\dfrac{7}{4}$

e. 2 hours

Problem Set 21

1. True
2. False
3. 4
4. -24.6
5. 49
6. 4
7. -3
8. Yes
9. No
10. $3x-8$
11. 4
12. $3x-3$
13. $\dfrac{1}{8}$
14. $-\dfrac{x}{2}$
15. $\dfrac{5x}{x+7}$
16. $-\dfrac{12}{5}$
17. 1
18. $\dfrac{3}{14}$
19. $-\dfrac{1}{2}$
20. -6
21. $\dfrac{11}{3}$
22. 1 hour

Practice 22

a. Yes

b. $\dfrac{11x-9}{9x+27}$

c. $\dfrac{5}{7}$

d. $\dfrac{1}{10}$

e. 5.7 gallons

Problem Set 22

1. True
2. False
3. -7
4. 21
5. 7
6. -20
7. 3
8. Yes
9. Yes
10. $\dfrac{3}{8}$
11. $2x-2$
12. $\dfrac{5x-15}{2x-10}$
13. $\dfrac{7x-4}{4x+8}$
14. $\dfrac{x}{2}$
15. $9x-12$
16. $\dfrac{5}{8}$
17. $\dfrac{5}{3}$
18. $\dfrac{29}{7}$
19. -1
20. $\dfrac{3}{14}$
21. $\dfrac{1}{3}$
22. 75 cartons

Practice 23

a. $-4+9x$

b. $-\dfrac{9}{5}$

c. $\dfrac{2}{25}$

d. -9

e. 24 degrees

Problem Set 23

1. True
2. True
3. 11
4. 30
5. -22
6. -3
7. 20
8. Yes
9. No
10. $\dfrac{1}{4}$
11. $-2+3x$
12. 0
13. $-\dfrac{4}{3}$
14. $7x-\dfrac{2}{5}$
15. $48x$
16. 5
17. $\dfrac{2}{9}$
18. 18
19. -2
20. $\dfrac{5}{14}$
21. $-\dfrac{38}{5}$
22. 30 degrees

CHAPTER 4

Practice 24
a. 2.89
b. Yes
c. $(x-1)^3$ cubic inches
d. -1
e. 5 balcony tickets

Problem Set 24
1. True
2. False
3. False
4. 2
5. 64
6. 3
7. 12.25
8. -50
9. No
10. Yes
11. x^2 square inches
12. $(x+4)^3$ cubic centimeters
13. -1
14. $\frac{3}{4}x-2$
15. $9x$
16. $-\frac{3x}{x-3}$
17. $\frac{9x+2}{6x+9}$
18. -25
19. 5
20. $\frac{4}{3}$
21. -2
22. -16
23. 6 packages

Practice 25
a. 9
b. $(3x)^3$ cubic inches

c. $-2y^2+3$
d. 17
e. 33

Problem Set 25
1. True
2. True
3. 64
4. $\frac{1}{125}$
5. 9
6. -4
7. -10
8. No
9. Yes
10. $\left(\frac{x}{3}\right)^2$ square inches
11. $(5x)^3$ cubic centimeters
12. $7x^3$
13. $-3y^2+7$
14. -1
15. $\frac{5}{2}$
16. $\frac{8x+3}{2x+4}$
17. -5
18. 9
19. 0
20. -3
21. 7
22. 86

Practice 26
a. -48
b. $-\frac{7}{12}x^2$
c. $8x^6$
d. $-\frac{8}{3}$
e. 1.6 hours

Problem Set 26

1. True
2. True
3. False
4. 256
5. -17
6. 2^5 or 32
7. -50
8. $-\dfrac{1}{27}$
9. Yes
10. No
11. $-\dfrac{5}{6}x^2$
12. x^7
13. $x^5 - 9x^4$
14. $\dfrac{-4x - 17}{4x}$
15. $\dfrac{3x^2 + 6x}{8x + 8}$
16. $25x^6$
17. 12
18. $\dfrac{3}{2}$
19. 1
20. $\dfrac{14}{3}$
21. 1 hour

Practice 27

a. Yes
b. $x^2 + 3x + 2$ square centimeters
c. $-2x^2 + 2x$
d. $x^3 + 7x^2 + 16x + 12$
e. $30,000,000

Problem Set 27

1. False
2. True
3. $\dfrac{1}{25}$
4. -1
5. -4
6. 10
7. 74.088
8. No
9. Yes
10. $49x^4$ square inches
11. $x^2 + 7x + 12$ square centimeters
12. $-3x^3$
13. $36x^8$
14. 6
15. $\dfrac{-9x}{2x - 18}$
16. $-3x^2 + 3x$
17. $x^3 + 6x^2 + 9x + 4$
18. -4
19. 27
20. $-\dfrac{4}{5}$
21. $\dfrac{9}{4}$
22. $2,000

Practice 28

a. -16
b. $27x^6$ cubic inches
c. $\dfrac{1}{y^5}$
d. $x^3 + (-10x^2) + 31x + (-30)$
e. 2.5 ounces

Problem Set 28

1. True
2. True
3. -81
4. 6
5. 1
6. -6
7. -8
8. Yes
9. No

10. $6x^2 - 5x - 4$ square feet
11. $8x^6$ cubic inches
12. $x^5 + 16x^3$
13. $-\dfrac{5}{9}x^4$
14. $\dfrac{3x}{2}$
15. $\dfrac{1}{y^4}$
16. $59{,}049z^{10}$
17. $x^3 + (-8x^2) + 19x + (-12)$
18. -6
19. 7
20. $\dfrac{10}{3}$
21. $\dfrac{20}{3}$
22. 6 ounces

Practice 29
a. Yes
b. Yes
c. $\dfrac{x^3}{-5x+2}$
d. $\dfrac{1}{x-5}$
e. 2 hours

Problem Set 29
1. False
2. True
3. 38
4. 1
5. 0
6. -36
7. -27
8. Yes
9. Yes
10. $13x^3 - 5x$
11. y^{11}

12. $\dfrac{x^2}{2}$
13. $10x^2 - 43x - 9$
14. $\dfrac{x^3}{-2x+3}$
15. $\dfrac{1}{x-8}$
16. 0
17. 10
18. -4
19. $\dfrac{2}{5}$
20. $\dfrac{6}{5}$
21. 1 hour

Practice 30
a. No
b. $x + 2$
c. $\dfrac{48y^3 - 2}{5y^2 + 15y}$
d. $\dfrac{x-3}{x}$
e. 12 gallons

Problem Set 30
1. True
2. False
3. 10^7 or 10,000,000
4. 10
5. 6^2 or 36
6. 19
7. -10
8. Yes
9. No
10. $\dfrac{2}{3x^3}$
11. $\dfrac{x^2 + 8x + 12}{20x^5}$
12. $x + 3$

13. $\dfrac{14y^3 - 5}{3y^2 + 6y}$

14. $4x^5 - 4x^3$

15. $\dfrac{x-2}{x}$

16. 2

17. -11

18. $-\dfrac{7}{2}$

19. $\dfrac{13}{3}$

20. -2

21. 40 gallons

16. $\dfrac{10}{x^4}$

17. $\dfrac{9x+6}{x^2+4x+4}$

18. -14

19. -7

20. -2

21. $\dfrac{8}{9}$

22. 32 nickels

Practice 31

a. 3.4×10^{-9}

b. 6.3×10^{12}

c. 2.05×10^{-4}

d. $\dfrac{20x + 15}{x^2 + 6x + 9}$

e. 12 dimes

Problem Set 31

1. True
2. False
3. False
4. 2.3×10^8
5. 1.7×10^{-9}
6. 9.5×10^{12}
7. 1.305×10^{29}
8. 2×10^{-14}
9. 2.86×10^{-4}
10. No
11. Yes
12. $10x^7$
13. $x^2 + 3x$
14. $\dfrac{3x}{4}$
15. $y^2 - 3y - 28$

CHAPTER 5

Practice 32

a. 258,000,000,000
b. 4
c. $2x^3(2x-7)$
d. $(x-8)(x-4)$
e. 6 years old

Problem Set 32

1. True
2. False
3. 895,000,000,000
4. 0.0000000506
5. 6
6. 2.73×10^{27}
7. 9
8. 3
9. 0
10. $2 \cdot 2 \cdot 3 \cdot 3 \cdot y \cdot y \cdot y \cdot y \cdot y$
11. $5x^3(3x-5)$
12. $(x-7)(x-3)$
13. Yes
14. Yes
15. 6
16. $\dfrac{1}{4}$
17. $10x^2 + 6x - 5$
18. $\dfrac{x^2}{2}$
19. $\dfrac{8y+20}{y^2+8y+7}$
20. Identity
21. $\dfrac{2}{15}$
22. 5
23. 12 years old

Practice 33

a. 1.56×10^{-12}
b. Rational

c. Irrational
d. 2.24
e. $350

Problem Set 33

1. True
2. True
3. True
4. 2.38×10^{12}
5. 9.2×10^{-10}
6. 1.5×10^{-5}
7. -4
8. 4
9. 2.68×10^{-12}
10. Rational
11. Irrational
12. 2.65
13. 3.32
14. Yes
15. No
16. $6x^2 - 5x - 4$
17. $\dfrac{3x^2}{2}$
18. $40z^8$
19. 3
20. 1
21. $-\dfrac{8}{3}$
22. $15

Practice 34

a. $\sqrt{2}$
b. $\sqrt[3]{35}$
c. Rational
d. $\dfrac{y-3}{2}$
e. 40 nickels

Problem Set 34

1. True
2. True

3. 2.39

4. 0.0000075

5. $\sqrt{35}$

6. 1.176×10^{19}

7. $\sqrt{5}$

8. 2

9. $\sqrt[3]{36}$

10. $7z^2(1+3z^2)$

11. $(x-8)(x-4)$

12. $(y-6)(y-7)$

13. Rational

14. Irrational

15. No

16. Yes

17. $-2x^2-5$

18. $\dfrac{x+5}{3x^2+3x-6}$

19. $\dfrac{y-2}{5}$

20. 31

21. $-\dfrac{9}{5}$

22. $\dfrac{3}{2}$

23. 38 dimes

Practice 35

a. $\sqrt{10}+\sqrt{11}$

b. $\sqrt[3]{5}$

c. $5\sqrt{7}$

d. $8\sqrt{3}$

e. $8,000

Problem Set 35

1. False

2. False

3. 0.000042

4. 1,835,000

5. 2.59×10^8

6. 6.53×10^{-10}

7. $\sqrt{6}+\sqrt{7}$

8. $\sqrt{22}$

9. $\sqrt[3]{4}$

10. $3\sqrt{8}$

11. $\sqrt[3]{45}$

12. $10\sqrt{2}$

13. Irrational

14. Rational

15. Yes

16. No

17. $7x^4-14x$

18. $4y^2-21y-18$

19. $\dfrac{x-3}{x+2}$

20. $\dfrac{5z+15}{8z-16}$

21. 1

22. 4

23. 12

24. $15,000

Practice 36

a. $7\sqrt{2}$

b. $2\sqrt[3]{9}$

c. $6\sqrt[3]{2}$

d. $\dfrac{5}{y+2}$

e. 90

Problem Set 36

1. True

2. False

3. 2.35×10^{-6}

4. 9.9×10^{12}

5. 3.87

6. 4.58

7. $\sqrt{57}$

8. $\sqrt[3]{3}$

9. $5\sqrt{2}$

10. $3\sqrt[3]{2}$
11. $4\sqrt[3]{2}$
12. $5x^2(x+3)$
13. $(x+5)(x+4)$
14. $(x-10)(x+6)$
15. $7x^4 - x^2$
16. $125x^6$
17. $\dfrac{5 - 6z + 7z^2}{z^3}$
18. $\dfrac{x-7}{x-2}$
19. $\dfrac{5}{y+1}$
20. $\dfrac{4}{23}$
21. 2
22. 6
23. 40

Practice 37
a. $9\sqrt{2}$
b. $\sqrt{14} - \sqrt{21}$
c. $21\sqrt{5} + 20\sqrt{3}$
d. $-4\sqrt{14} + 10$
e. 4 hours

Problem Set 37
1. True
2. True
3. 3.68×10^{23}
4. 2.52×10^{-2}
5. 8×10^5
6. $4\sqrt{5}$
7. $5\sqrt[4]{7}$
8. $\sqrt{15} - \sqrt{6}$
9. $\sqrt[4]{3}$
10. $4\sqrt{5} + 15\sqrt{2}$
11. $5\sqrt{6} + (-63)$

12. Yes
13. No
14. $x^2 - x - 72$
15. $-x^4$
16. $\dfrac{1}{16y^{10}}$
17. $\dfrac{3x}{x+1}$
18. $\dfrac{2}{y^2 - 2y}$
19. 2
20. 1
21. 4
22. 2 hours

Practice 38
a. $\dfrac{\sqrt{15}}{6}$
b. $\dfrac{\sqrt[3]{99}}{3}$
c. $-\dfrac{3\sqrt{2} - 3\sqrt{6}}{4}$
d. $-2\sqrt{55} + 16$
e. 12 years old

Problem Set 38
1. True
2. True
3. 88,100,000
4. 0.000035
5. $3\sqrt[3]{2}$
6. $\dfrac{\sqrt{6}}{4}$
7. $6\sqrt{2}$
8. $3\sqrt{10}$
9. $\dfrac{\sqrt[3]{20}}{2}$

10. $-\dfrac{4\sqrt{2}-4\sqrt{7}}{5}$

11. $6\sqrt{3}+3\sqrt{2}$

12. $-2\sqrt{15}+8$

13. $6z(5-z^2)$

14. $(x+1)(x+9)$

15. Yes

16. Yes

17. $-16.1x^3$

18. $21x^8$

19. $\dfrac{4}{5z^3}$

20. $\dfrac{y^2-10y+25}{y^2+2y}$

21. -2

22. $\dfrac{13}{5}$

23. $\dfrac{13}{7}$

24. 10 years old

Practice 39

a. $4^{\frac{5}{3}}$

b. 4

c. $6^{\frac{5}{6}}$

d. $5^{\frac{1}{4}}$

e. 57

Problem Set 39

1. True

2. True

3. $8^{\frac{1}{2}}$

4. $12^{\frac{1}{4}}$

5. $2^{\frac{4}{3}}$

6. $\sqrt{105}$

7. 3

8. $\sqrt{5}$

9. $2\sqrt[4]{17}$

10. $\dfrac{\sqrt{22}}{11}$

11. $5^{\frac{5}{6}}$

12. $7^{\frac{1}{4}}$

13. $9y^2(9+y)$

14. $(x+9)(x+2)$

15. $81x^{12}$

16. $\dfrac{30}{y^7}$

17. $\dfrac{5}{6}x^3-\dfrac{1}{2}$

18. $x^5+(-7x^2)$

19. $\dfrac{3}{y-1}$

20. $\dfrac{7}{3}$

21. 3

22. $-\dfrac{3}{5}$

23. 73

CHAPTER 6

Practice 40

a. $-\dfrac{\sqrt{10}+\sqrt{14}}{2}$

b. $4^{\frac{7}{15}}$

c. $x^3+(-5x^2)+2x+8$

d. $+\sqrt{11}, -\sqrt{11}$

e. 200 gallons

Problem Set 40

1. True
2. True
3. True
4. 9.25×10^{17}
5. 3.37×10^{-13}
6. $\sqrt{6}$
7. $9\sqrt{3}$
8. $\sqrt{14}$
9. $-\dfrac{\sqrt{6}+\sqrt{15}}{3}$
10. $11^{\frac{7}{12}}$
11. $5^{\frac{7}{15}}$
12. $6(x+3)$
13. $(x-12)(x-4)$
14. $\dfrac{1+x^2}{x^2+2x}$
15. x^3-2x^2-5x+6
16. $\dfrac{1}{x^{10}}$
17. -7
18. $5, -5$
19. $\dfrac{10}{3}$
20. $9, -9$
21. $\dfrac{4}{5}$
22. $+\sqrt{7}, -\sqrt{7}$

23. 3.75 pounds

Practice 41

a. -5.83

b. $\dfrac{5\sqrt{2}+\sqrt{6}}{22}$

c. $+\sqrt{10}-1, -\sqrt{10}-1$

d. $+\sqrt{5}, -\sqrt{5}$

e. 7, 21

Problem Set 41

1. True
2. True
3. 3.24
4. -5.16
5. $\sqrt{22}+\sqrt{6}$
6. $2\sqrt{5}$
7. $\dfrac{\sqrt[3]{6}}{2}$
8. $\dfrac{7\sqrt{3}+\sqrt{6}}{47}$
9. $3^{\frac{9}{10}}$
10. $6^{\frac{5}{4}}$
11. No
12. Yes
13. $8x^4$
14. $2x^3-14x$
15. $\dfrac{x+1}{x^2}$
16. $+3, -3$
17. -1
18. $+\sqrt{5}-2, -\sqrt{5}-2$
19. $-\dfrac{4}{3}$
20. $+\sqrt{3}, -\sqrt{3}$
21. $+\sqrt{13}, -\sqrt{13}$
22. 5, 10

Practice 42

a. $5\sqrt{7}-17$
b. 5
c. 0, 7
d. -3, -4
e. 6 in., 18 in.

Problem Set 42

1. True
2. True
3. 1.155×10^{-6}
4. 9×10^{-8}
5. $\sqrt[3]{36}$
6. $8^{\frac{5}{6}}$
7. $\sqrt{10}$
8. $3\sqrt{6}-22$
9. $2^{\frac{13}{6}}$
10. $3x(x-3)$
11. $(x+6)(x+2)$
12. $(x-9)(x+5)$
13. $\dfrac{3}{x^8}$
14. x^3+5x^2+8x+6
15. $\dfrac{1}{7}$
16. $+\sqrt{19}$, $-\sqrt{19}$
17. 8
18. $+2\sqrt{3}$, $-2\sqrt{3}$
19. 0, 4
20. 0, 3
21. -2, -4
22. 24 ft., 3 ft.

Practice 43

a. $-6\sqrt{5}+(-6\sqrt{11})$
b. $(2x+3)(x+4)$
c. $-\dfrac{1}{3}$, -5

d. $\dfrac{1}{5}$, -2
e. 9 ft., 15 ft.

Problem Set 43

1. False
2. False
3. -1.26
4. -18.24
5. $\sqrt[5]{4}$
6. $9\sqrt{10}$
7. $-24\sqrt{3}+(-24\sqrt{5})$
8. $5^{\frac{13}{12}}$
9. $9x(2x+1)$
10. $(x+7)(x+2)$
11. $(3x+2)(x+3)$
12. $\dfrac{64}{x^6}$
13. $5x^2-7x+2$
14. $\dfrac{1}{2}$
15. 5, -5
16. 3
17. 1, -7
18. 0, $-\dfrac{1}{2}$
19. $-\dfrac{1}{2}$, -3
20. $\dfrac{1}{3}$, -2
21. 6 ft., 10 ft.

Practice 44

a. $\dfrac{\sqrt{6}}{2}$
b. $+2\sqrt{3}$, $-2\sqrt{3}$
c. $+\sqrt{19}-5$, $-\sqrt{19}-5$
d. $+\sqrt{13.5}+4$, $-\sqrt{13.5}+4$

e. 13 ft.

Problem Set 44

1. True
2. True
3. 7.92×10^{18}
4. 1.05×10^{-11}
5. $2^{\frac{3}{5}}$
6. $\sqrt[6]{3}$
7. $\dfrac{\sqrt{6}}{3}$
8. $9x^2(x+5)$
9. $(x-9)(x+6)$
10. $(5x+2)(x+3)$
11. Yes
12. Yes
13. $x^2+(-7x)+10$
14. $\dfrac{1}{z^8}$
15. $\dfrac{3x^2}{2}$
16. $\dfrac{20}{3}$
17. $+2\sqrt{5}, -2\sqrt{5}$
18. $0, 2$
19. $+\sqrt{13}-4, -\sqrt{13}-4$
20. $+\sqrt{4.5}+3, -\sqrt{4.5}+3$
21. 7 ft.

Problem Set 45

1. True
2. True
3. 2.52
4. -0.02
5. $2\sqrt[3]{2}$
6. $8^{\frac{13}{20}}$
7. $5^{\frac{1}{3}}$
8. $2x(8-9x)$
9. $(x-5)(x-5)$
10. $(5x+2)(x-4)$
11. $24x^3-12x^2$
12. $\dfrac{2}{x-4}$
13. $30x^6$
14. $\dfrac{10+3x}{8x^2}$
15. $+3\sqrt{2}, -3\sqrt{2}$
16. -3
17. $0, \dfrac{1}{3}$
18. $10, 1$
19. $\dfrac{-13+\sqrt{29}}{10}, \dfrac{-13-\sqrt{29}}{10}$
20. $\dfrac{5+\sqrt{133}}{6}, \dfrac{5-\sqrt{133}}{6}$
21. 3 ft.

Practice 45

a. 0.46
b. $(3x+2)(x-5)$
c. $\dfrac{-11+\sqrt{61}}{6}, \dfrac{-11-\sqrt{61}}{6}$
d. $\dfrac{3+\sqrt{33}}{6}, \dfrac{3-\sqrt{33}}{6}$
e. 2 ft.

21

CHAPTER 7

Practice 46
a. $a = -3$, $b = -5$, $c = -1$
b. $5\sqrt{10} - 5\sqrt{5}$
c. 9
d. $-\dfrac{3}{2}, -4$
e. 76 women

Problem Set 46
1. True
2. True
3. $a = 3$, $b = 7$, $c = 2$
4. $a = -2$, $b = -9$, $c = -4$
5. 3
6. $5\sqrt{21}$
7. $9\sqrt{7} - 9\sqrt{2}$
8. $-5x(x + 7)$
9. $(x - 7)(x - 2)$
10. $(3x + 2)(x + 4)$
11. $\dfrac{2}{x^2 - x}$
12. $2x^2 + x - 10$
13. $\dfrac{7 - 6x}{16x^3}$
14. 4
15. $-\dfrac{9}{4}$
16. 64
17. $5, -5$
18. $0, 2$
19. $4, 3$
20. $-\dfrac{5}{3}, -3$
21. 154 guests

Practice 47
a. 64
b. $\dfrac{1}{60}$
c. 16
d. $\dfrac{-3 + \sqrt{17}}{2}$, $\dfrac{-3 - \sqrt{17}}{2}$
e. 12, 14

Problem Set 47
1. False
2. True
3. -0.81
4. 1.04
5. 4.4×10^{-9}
6. 6×10^8
7. $\dfrac{2}{5}\sqrt{7}$
8. $6^{\frac{5}{6}}$
9. $2^{\frac{1}{20}}$
10. $9(5 - x)$
11. $6y(y^2 + 2)$
12. $(x + 7)(x + 6)$
13. 18
14. $\dfrac{2x}{3}$
15. $12z^2 - 18z$
16. 9
17. $-\dfrac{1}{18}$
18. 36
19. $0, -32$
20. 4, 5
21. $\dfrac{-3 + \sqrt{29}}{2}$, $\dfrac{-3 - \sqrt{29}}{2}$

22. 16, 18

Practice 48
a. $-\dfrac{5}{y - 3}$
b. 11
c. 48
d. $\dfrac{-1 + \sqrt{34}}{3}$, $\dfrac{-1 - \sqrt{34}}{3}$
e. 182 quarters

Problem Set 48
1. $a = -4$, $b = 7$, $c = -9$
2. $a = 3$, $b = -1$, $c = -1$
3. 402,500,000
4. 0.00003009
5. $6\sqrt[3]{3}$
6. $4\sqrt{6}$
7. $\sqrt[4]{55}$
8. Yes
9. No
10. $\dfrac{1}{25z^6}$
11. $\dfrac{1}{9x^3}$
12. $-\dfrac{2}{y - 2}$
13. $6x$
14. 7
15. -7
16. 50
17. 5
18. $0, \dfrac{1}{2}$
19. $-1, -7$
20. $\dfrac{-2 + \sqrt{14}}{5}$, $\dfrac{-2 - \sqrt{14}}{5}$
21. 16 nickels

Practice 49

a. $\dfrac{2}{x^2 + (-6x) + 8}$

b. 4 (-1 is extraneous)

c. $4, 5$

d. $-\dfrac{1}{7}$

e. 16 years old

Problem Set 49

1. True
2. False
3. 7.54×10^{-8}
4. 2.35×10^{15}
5. $9\sqrt{2}$
6. $3^{\frac{26}{15}}$
7. $7^{\frac{1}{6}}$
8. $7x^4(2x - 1)$
9. $(x - 9)(x + 8)$
10. $(3x - 5)(x + 3)$
11. $\dfrac{3}{4}x^3$
12. $\dfrac{7}{x + 4}$
13. $-\dfrac{2}{x^2 - 4x + 3}$
14. 5 (2 is extraneous)
15. $-2, -3$
16. 2
17. $0, -2$
18. 11
19. 9
20. $-\dfrac{4}{9}$
21. 11 years old

Practice 50

a. $\dfrac{1}{x - 2}$

b. 18

c. $\dfrac{13}{4}$

d. $-8, 5$

e. $\$20,000$

Problem Set 50

1. -2.00
2. 6.72
3. $-8\sqrt{7}$
4. $5^{\frac{5}{14}}$
5. $2\sqrt{2} + \sqrt{3}$
6. $21x(1 - 2x)$
7. $(y - 6)(y + 3)$
8. $(3x + 7)(x - 6)$
9. No
10. Yes
11. $11x^6$
12. $-2x^3 - 6x$
13. $\dfrac{1}{x - 3}$
14. 12
15. -1
16. $\dfrac{29}{2}$
17. 5
18. $0, -8$
19. $-9, 7$
20. $\$30,000$

Practice 51

a. $\dfrac{1}{x + 4}$

b. 6 (-1 is extraneous)

c. 2

d. $-\dfrac{6 + \sqrt{34}}{2}$, $-\dfrac{6 - \sqrt{34}}{2}$

e. 12 hours

Problem Set 51

1. $a = 2$, $b = 3$, $c = -1$
2. $a = 1$, $b = -4$, $c = 5$
3. $20,600,000$
4. 0.000071
5. $\sqrt{2}$
6. $6^{\frac{11}{12}}$
7. $11^{\frac{7}{4}}$
8. $3x(x - 3)$
9. $6x^2(x^2 + 4)$
10. $(y + 6)(y + 2)$
11. $-3x^2$
12. $2x^2 - x - 3$
13. $\dfrac{1}{x + 5}$
14. 7
15. 21
16. 5 (-2 is extraneous)
17. 3
18. $-\dfrac{5}{3}$
19. $-\dfrac{5 + \sqrt{23}}{2}$, $-\dfrac{5 - \sqrt{23}}{2}$
20. 60 seconds

CHAPTER 8

Practice 52

a. $-\sqrt{13}i$

b. $\dfrac{2}{5}i$

c. $7i$, $-7i$

d. $-\dfrac{4+\sqrt{15}}{2}$, $-\dfrac{4-\sqrt{15}}{2}$

e. 30 degrees

Problem Set 52

1. True
2. False
3. 4.55
4. 1.51
5. $5i$
6. $6i$
7. $-\sqrt{11}i$
8. $\dfrac{3}{4}i$
9. $7x^2(3-4x)$
10. $(x-6)(x-3)$
11. $(2x+3)(x+1)$
12. $\dfrac{x-4}{2}$
13. $40x^8$
14. $\dfrac{2y}{y-3}$
15. 0 , $\dfrac{1}{3}$
16. 81
17. $\dfrac{17}{2}$
18. -13
19. 1 (-4 is extraneous)
20. $3i$, $-3i$

21. $-\dfrac{9+\sqrt{69}}{6}$, $-\dfrac{9-\sqrt{69}}{6}$

22. 12 degrees

Practice 53

a. $\dfrac{1}{3}i$

b. $2\sqrt{5}i$

c. $4i$, $-4i$

d. No solutions (9 is extraneous)

e. 4 hours

Problem Set 53

1. True
2. False
3. 8.362×10^{13}
4. 5×10^{-7}
5. 8
6. -58
7. $8i$
8. $\dfrac{1}{2}i$
9. $3\sqrt{2}i$
10. $5y^4(4y+5)$
11. $(x+7)(x-6)$
12. $(z-7)(z+3)$
13. $-5x^3+2x$
14. $2x^6+10x^4$
15. $\dfrac{3x}{x+3}$
16. 48
17. 4
18. $5i$, $-5i$
19. $3, 2$
20. 1
21. No solutions (16 is extraneous)

22. 4 hours

Practice 54

a. $\sqrt{1.5}i$

b. $\dfrac{3}{7}i$

c. $-3\sqrt{3}i$

d. 4 (1 is extraneous)

e. 60 pounds

Problem Set 54

1. 3,950,000,000
2. 0.0002875
3. $-10i$
4. $\sqrt{2.5}i$
5. $5\sqrt{2}i$
6. $4i$
7. $\dfrac{3}{5}i$
8. $-2\sqrt{6}i$
9. $y^3(1-2y)$
10. $(x+5)(x+6)$
11. $(3x-2)(x-5)$
12. $\dfrac{1}{49y^{16}}$
13. $\dfrac{7x-2}{6x-12}$
14. $\dfrac{1}{4x}$
15. 4
16. 7
17. $\sqrt{19}i$, $-\sqrt{19}i$
18. $\dfrac{17}{5}$
19. $4, 2$
20. $5, -5$
21. False equation (2 and 1 are extraneous)
22. 37.5 pounds

24

Practice 55
a. 36
b. 3
c. $-2,187i$
d. -2 (-7 is extraneous)
e. 150 seconds

Problem Set 55
1. 30
2. 14
3. $9i$
4. $2\sqrt{2}i$
5. $19i$
6. $3.8i$
7. 35
8. 2
9. 81
10. $-128i$
11. $9x(x-4)$
12. $(x+9)(x+5)$
13. x^3-4x^2+5x-2
14. $-z^4$
15. $-\dfrac{5y^2}{2}$
16. $-\dfrac{15}{4}$
17. 32
18. $0, -11$
19. -2 (-5 is extraneous)
20. 14
21. $4\sqrt{5}i, -4\sqrt{5}i$
22. 225 minutes

Practice 56
a. $-1+1i$ or $-1+i$
b. $0+(-7i)$
c. $\dfrac{3\sqrt{5}}{5}$

d. $\dfrac{1}{2}, 1$
e. 5 years

Problem Set 56
1. True
2. True
3. $1+1i$ or $1+i$
4. $0+(-8i)$
5. $11i$
6. $2\sqrt{14}i$
7. $-\sqrt{42}$
8. $\dfrac{2\sqrt{3}}{3}$
9. $-32i$
10. $-64i$
11. $5x^2(x^2+3)$
12. $(x-7)(x+4)$
13. $\dfrac{1}{7}x^3-x^2$
14. $\dfrac{3x}{5}$
15. $\dfrac{1}{x+4}$
16. -9
17. 29
18. $0, -4$
19. $\dfrac{3}{2}$
20. $2\sqrt{3}i, -2\sqrt{3}i$
21. $\dfrac{1}{3}, 1$
22. 6 years

Practice 57
a. $6+6i$
b. 12
c. 4 (1 is extraneous)
d. $\sqrt{5}i, -\sqrt{5}i$
e. 17 feet

Problem Set 57
1. True
2. True
3. -39
4. -5
5. $-1+(-1i)$ or $-1+(-i)$
6. $0+\dfrac{3}{5}i$
7. $-2i$
8. $3\sqrt{7}i$
9. $-5i$
10. $7+7i$
11. -40
12. 14
13. $x^2(x^2-10)$
14. $(y-5)(y-5)$
15. $2x+3$
16. $-1.5y^3+6y$
17. 2
18. -1
19. 9 (1 is extraneous)
20. $\sqrt{7}i, -\sqrt{7}i$
21. 31 feet

Practice 58
a. 1
b. $10+10i$
c. $-5+3i, -5+(-3i)$
d. $2+i, 2+(-i)$
e. 100

Problem Set 58
1. 8.205×10^6
2. 9×10^{-2}
3. $\sqrt{17}i$
4. $3\sqrt{10}i$
5. $25i$
6. $-\dfrac{2}{7}$

7. $-1+(-3i)$
8. 1
9. $18+13i$
10. $(x-7)(x+5)$
11. $(3y-2)(y+1)$
12. $\dfrac{1}{16x^4}$
13. $\dfrac{7+4z^2}{6z^3}$
14. x^3-3x^2-9x-5
15. -2
16. 33
17. $-7+4i$, $-7+(-4i)$
18. $-\dfrac{3}{5}$
19. $1+i$, $1+(-i)$
20. $0,2$
21. 91

14. $\dfrac{x^3}{14}$
15. $\dfrac{6}{x^2}$
16. 25
17. -3
18. 4 $(-1$ is extraneous$)$
19. $\sqrt{6}i$, $-\sqrt{6}i$
20. $-1+3i$, $-1+(-3i)$
21. 126

Practice 59
a. Real solutions
b. Complex solutions
c. 6 $(-2$ is extraneous$)$
d. $2+5i$, $2+(-5i)$
e. 112

Problem Set 59
1. True
2. True
3. Real solutions
4. Complex solutions
5. $5i$
6. $3\sqrt{5}i$
7. $-9i$
8. $-2\sqrt{3}$
9. $-7i$
10. $-13+13i$
11. $5(y^2-5)$
12. $(x-8)(x+3)$
13. $10z^{11}$

CHAPTER 9

Practice 60
a. $3 + (-2i)$
b. $-6 + 12i$
c. $0, -1, -3$
d. $4, 1, 0$
e. $32

Problem Set 60
1. -2
2. -13
3. Complex solutions
4. Real solutions
5. $\sqrt{2}i$
6. $\frac{1}{3}i$
7. $1 + (-2i)$
8. $27i$
9. $2\sqrt{3}$
10. $-10 + 4i$
11. $-18(x + 5)$
12. $(2x + 1)(x + 5)$
13. $-3y^6$
14. $\dfrac{x + 2}{8x^3}$
15. $\dfrac{x - 3}{x - 2}$
16. $-\dfrac{4}{3}$
17. $0, -1, -2$
18. 8
19. $\sqrt{11}i, -\sqrt{11}i$
20. $3, 2, 0$
21. $2

Practice 61
a. $1 + 8i$
b. $x(x + 6)(x + 1)$
c. $6, 0, -3$

d. $\sqrt{3}, -\sqrt{3}, \sqrt{6}, -\sqrt{6}$
e. 5 hours

Problem Set 61
1. $48{,}000{,}000$
2. 0.001125
3. Complex solutions
4. Real solutions
5. $\sqrt{29}i$
6. $6\sqrt{3}i$
7. $-3 + 8i$
8. 44
9. $\sqrt{15}$
10. $-1 + 3i$
11. $(x - 3)(x + 1)$
12. $x(x + 3)(x + 2)$
13. $\dfrac{x^{10}}{9}$
14. $\dfrac{y - 3}{3y^5}$
15. $\dfrac{11}{5}$
16. $5, 0, -3$
17. $-\dfrac{1}{4}$
18. -40
19. $\sqrt{3}, -\sqrt{3}, \sqrt{5}, -\sqrt{5}$
20. 7 hours

Practice 62
a. $(3x + 4)(x + 1)$
b. $(x^2 - 7)(x^2 + 2)$
c. $0, -3, -5$
d. $2, 1, -4$
e. 60 seconds

Problem Set 62
1. True
2. True
3. True
4. 0
5. -2
6. Real solutions
7. Real solutions
8. $9 + 2i$
9. -16
10. $\dfrac{1}{2}$
11. $-7 + 9i$
12. $(3x + 2)(x + 2)$
13. $(x^2 - 6)(x^2 + 2)$
14. $\dfrac{5}{7}x^3$
15. $\dfrac{4y}{y + 1}$
16. 20
17. 3
18. $0, -3, -4$
19. $\dfrac{21}{2}$
20. $1, -2, -3$
21. 250 seconds

Practice 63
a. $x^2(x - 8)(x + 2)$
b. $x^2 + (-2x) + 6$
c. $4x + 15 + \dfrac{30}{x - 3}$
d. $5, 1, -2$
e. 17

Problem Set 63
1. True
2. False
3. 1.215×10^{14}
4. 3.2×10^{-6}

5. $\dfrac{\sqrt{14}}{7}i$

6. $-2\sqrt{5}i$

7. $-18\sqrt{2}i$

8. $7x^3(2x^2-1)$

9. $(x-3)(x+2)$

10. $x^2(x-7)(x+3)$

11. $3z^5+12z^3$

12. $x^2+(-3x)+6$

13. $3x+11+\dfrac{7}{x-2}$

14. -3

15. $0,\dfrac{1}{2}$

16. -19

17. $4,0,-1$

18. 9

19. $4,1,-2$

20. 21

10. $(z^3-8)(z^3-1)$

11. $\dfrac{5}{8x}$

12. $\dfrac{1}{x+2}$

13. $\dfrac{1}{x^2-5x+2}$

14. $\dfrac{11}{14}$

15. $-1,-3$

16. $\sqrt{10},-\sqrt{10},\sqrt{2},-\sqrt{2}$

17. $-\dfrac{3}{2}$

18. $\dfrac{13}{5}$

19. $2,1,-2$

20. 4 feet

Practice 65

a. $2y^2+2y+1$

b. $x-4+-\dfrac{7}{x-2}$

c. $3,0,-4$

d. $2,\sqrt{3}i,-\sqrt{3}i$

e. 40 ounces

Problem Set 65

1. False
2. False
3. 7.52×10^5
4. 6.01×10^{-4}
5. $\dfrac{1}{2}i$
6. $-8+(-10i)$
7. $125i$
8. $-2(1+2x)$
9. $(x+7)(x+6)$
10. $x(x+2)(x+2)$

11. $-4x^4+6$

12. x^3-4x^2-21x

13. $2y^2+3y+1$

14. $x-2+-\dfrac{4}{x-3}$

15. -3

16. 6

17. $2\sqrt{3}i,-2\sqrt{3}i$

18. $2,0,-3$

19. $1,\sqrt{2}i,-\sqrt{2}i$

20. 50 ounces

Practice 66

a. -27

b. $(x^2+7)(x^2+3)$

c. y^2+4y+1

d. $1,0.5+0.5\sqrt{15}i,0.5-0.5\sqrt{15}i$

e. 24 feet

Problem Set 66

1. True
2. True
3. 10.83
4. -14.86
5. $2i$
6. $10\sqrt{2}i$
7. $\dfrac{5}{4}i$
8. -8
9. $17+33i$
10. $-3y^3(y+4)$
11. $(2x-3)(x+1)$
12. $(x^2+7)(x^2+4)$
13. $-16x+8x^3$
14. $\dfrac{1}{x+1}$
15. y^2+3y+4
16. -2

Practice 64

a. $(z^3-7)(z^3-1)$

b. $\dfrac{1}{x^2-6x+1}$

c. $\sqrt{11},-\sqrt{11},\sqrt{2},-\sqrt{2}$

d. $2,-1,-3$

e. 58 feet

Problem Set 64

1. True
2. False
3. -0.29
4. 3.68
5. $7+12.6i$
6. $24i$
7. $3+(-14i)$
8. $9x^2(1+5x^3)$
9. $(2y-3)(y+1)$

17. 8

18. 6

19. $3i, -3i$

20. $2, 0.5 + 0.5\sqrt{7}i,$
$0.5 - 0.5\sqrt{7}i$

21. 5 feet

CHAPTER 10

Practice 67

a. $x + (-4) + \dfrac{3}{x + (-5)}$

b. 4, 3, 0

c. $y = -3$

d. Yes

e. 11 quarters

Problem Set 67

1. True
2. True
3. True
4. $-7 + (-2i)$
5. $42i$
6. $27 + 23i$
7. $10y^6$
8. $-27x^3$
9. $\dfrac{x^2 + 2x}{3}$
10. $x + (-5) + \dfrac{5}{x + (-7)}$
11. $-\dfrac{16}{7}$
12. -5
13. 3, 2, 0
14. $y = 5$
15. $y = 7$
16. $y = 1$
17. Yes
18. No
19. Yes
20. 14 dimes

Practice 68

a. $x^2 + 3x + 6$

b. 0 (-5 is extraneous)

c. $y = 2x - 8$

d. $y = 5 - 3x$

e. $5,000

Problem Set 68

1. True
2. True
3. $5.7i$
4. $24 + (-12i)$
5. $3x(4x - 5)$
6. $(x - 7)(x - 6)$
7. $6x^2 + 7x - 20$
8. $x^2 + 3x + 8$
9. 44
10. -7
11. 0 (-3 is extraneous)
12. $y = -10$
13. $y = -1$
14. $y = -8$
15. No
16. Yes
17. Yes
18. $y = 2x$
19. $y = 3x - 15$
20. $y = 4 - 2x$
21. $50,000

Practice 69

a. and b.

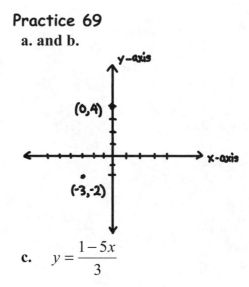

c. $y = \dfrac{1 - 5x}{3}$

d.

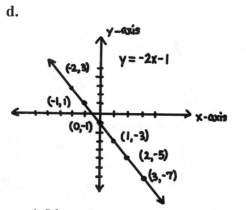

e. 1.5 hours

Problem Set 69

1. True
2. True
3. False
4. True
5. 7.5×10^7
6. 5.25×10^3
7. $\dfrac{1}{3y+6}$
8. $-32x^7$
9. 4
10. 8, -3

11. – 13.

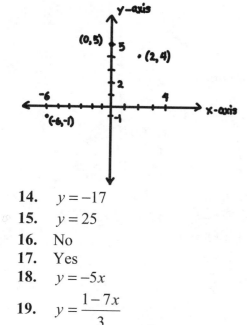

14. $y = -17$
15. $y = 25$
16. No
17. Yes
18. $y = -5x$
19. $y = \dfrac{1-7x}{3}$

20.

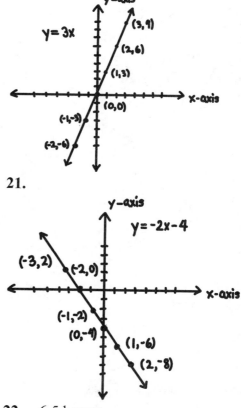

21.

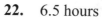

22. 6.5 hours

Practice 70

a. $(3x-7)(2x+1)$
b. 4, 0, -6
c. $y = 18 - 3x$
d.

e. 48 seconds

Problem Set 70

1. False
2. True
3. True
4. 47
5. -1
6. $(x-8)(x+7)$
7. $(3x-5)(2x+1)$
8. $\dfrac{2}{5}z^2$
9. $4x^5$
10. $-\dfrac{8}{3}$
11. $\dfrac{5}{3}$
12. $5, 0, -7$

13. and 14.

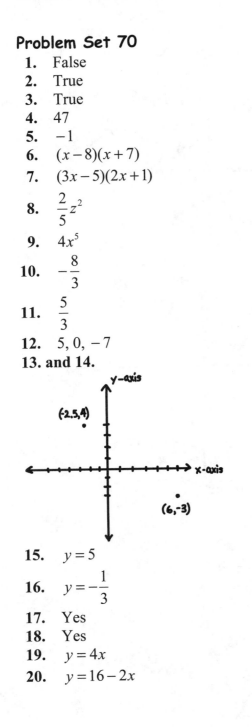

15. $y = 5$
16. $y = -\dfrac{1}{3}$
17. Yes
18. Yes
19. $y = 4x$
20. $y = 16 - 2x$

21.

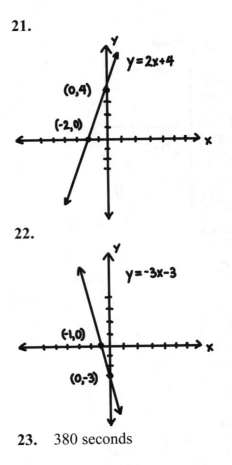

22.

23. 380 seconds

Practice 71

a. $y = -5$
b. $+3$
c. $+2$
d. $+1$
e. 28 degrees

Problem Set 71

1. True
2. True
3. -16
4. 25
5. $5x(x^2 - 2)$
6. $(x+2)(x+1)$
7. $-\dfrac{1}{64x^{21}}$
8. $\dfrac{3}{2x+6}$

9. -5

10. $\dfrac{10}{3}$

11. $\sqrt{17}\,,\ -\sqrt{17}$

12. $y = -22$

13. $y = -3$

14. $y = \dfrac{5}{3}x$

15. $y = \dfrac{x+9}{8}$

16.

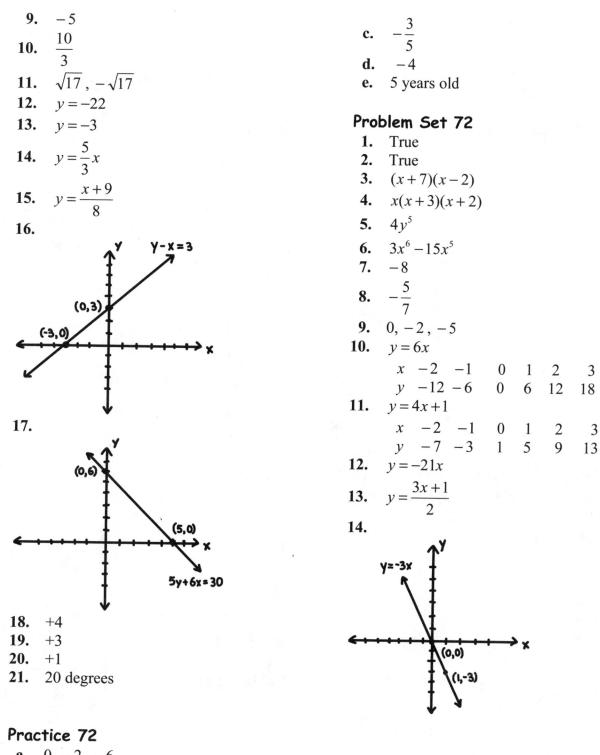

17.

18. $+4$

19. $+3$

20. $+1$

21. 20 degrees

Practice 72

a. $0,\ -2,\ -6$

b. $y = 5x + 2$

x	-2	-1	0	1	2	3
y	-8	-3	2	7	12	17

c. $-\dfrac{3}{5}$

d. -4

e. 5 years old

Problem Set 72

1. True

2. True

3. $(x+7)(x-2)$

4. $x(x+3)(x+2)$

5. $4y^5$

6. $3x^6 - 15x^5$

7. -8

8. $-\dfrac{5}{7}$

9. $0,\ -2,\ -5$

10. $y = 6x$

x	-2	-1	0	1	2	3
y	-12	-6	0	6	12	18

11. $y = 4x + 1$

x	-2	-1	0	1	2	3
y	-7	-3	1	5	9	13

12. $y = -21x$

13. $y = \dfrac{3x+1}{2}$

14.

15.

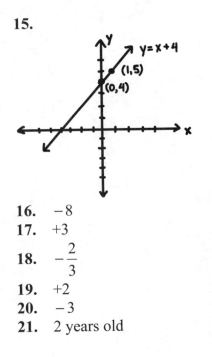

16. -8

17. $+3$

18. $-\dfrac{2}{3}$

19. $+2$

20. -3

21. 2 years old

Practice 73

a. $y^2 + 2y - 3$

b. $y - 5 = 3(x - 1)$

c. $y - 2 = 2(x - 4)$ or $y - 6 = 2(x - 6)$

d. Slope $+2$; y-intercept $(0,-5)$

e. 25 pounds

Problem Set 73

1. True
2. True
3. $8i$
4. $14 + (-5i)$
5. $-12x^{10}$
6. $\dfrac{1}{2x^2}$
7. $y^2 + 3y - 4$
8. 5
9. 1
10. 8, 0

11. and 12.

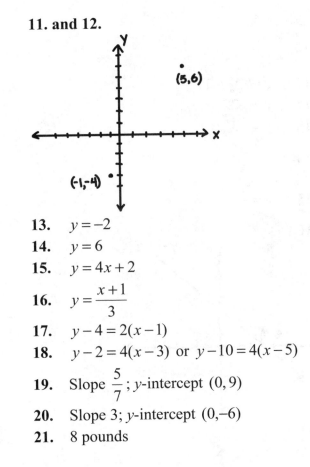

13. $y = -2$

14. $y = 6$

15. $y = 4x + 2$

16. $y = \dfrac{x + 1}{3}$

17. $y - 4 = 2(x - 1)$

18. $y - 2 = 4(x - 3)$ or $y - 10 = 4(x - 5)$

19. Slope $\dfrac{5}{7}$; y-intercept $(0, 9)$

20. Slope 3; y-intercept $(0, -6)$

21. 8 pounds

Practice 74

a. $-2 + \sqrt{6}$, $-2 - \sqrt{6}$

b. $+\dfrac{3}{2}$

c. $y = \dfrac{1}{2}x$

d. $y - 2 = 3(x - 1)$ or $y + 4 = 3(x + 1)$

e. $12,000

Problem Set 74

1. True
2. False
3. 9.628×10^8
4. 3.7×10^{-4}
5. $x^3 - 5x^2 - 6x + 16$
6. $\dfrac{-10x + 1}{8x^4}$

7. $-\dfrac{28}{3}$

8. $\dfrac{3}{2}$

9. $-3+\sqrt{10}$, $-3-\sqrt{10}$

10. $y=-5x$

x	-2	-1	0	1	2	3
y	10	5	0	-5	-10	-15

11. $y=\dfrac{1}{2}x+3$

x	-2	-1	0	1	2	3
y	2	$\dfrac{5}{2}$	3	$\dfrac{7}{2}$	4	$\dfrac{9}{2}$

12. $y=-3x+3$

13. $y=2x-7$

14.

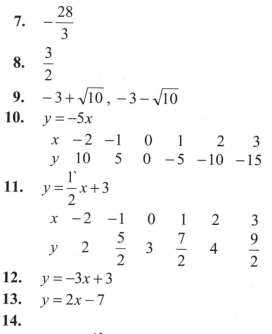

15.

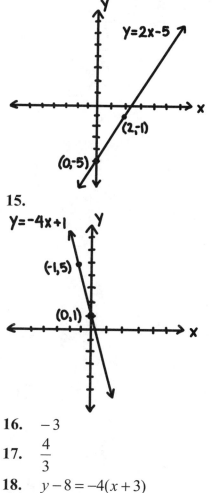

16. -3

17. $\dfrac{4}{3}$

18. $y-8=-4(x+3)$

19. $y=\dfrac{1}{3}x$

20. $y-1=2(x-2)$ or $y+5=2(x+1)$

21. \$45,000

Practice 75

a. $(x^2-9)(x^2+1)$

b. $3, 2, 1$

c. $y=37$

d. $y-7=\dfrac{3}{2}(x-5)$ or $y+8=\dfrac{3}{2}(x+5)$

e. 30 feet

Problem Set 75

1. True
2. False
3. -1
4. -2
5. $7x(x^3-7)$
6. $(x^2-10)(x^2+1)$
7. $11y^3-6y$
8. $\dfrac{2}{3x^2}$
9. 2
10. $-\dfrac{10}{3}$
11. $3, 1, -2$
12. $y=5$
13. $y=16$
14. $y=-\dfrac{x-4}{3}$
15. $y=\dfrac{7x}{2}$
16. $-\dfrac{2}{5}$
17. 1
18. $y=-\dfrac{3}{4}x+6$
19. $y+4=2(x+2)$

20. $y - 3 = \frac{3}{2}(x - 1)$ or $y + 9 = \frac{3}{2}(x + 7)$

21. 36 inches

Practice 76

a. Perpendicular

b. Horizontal

c.

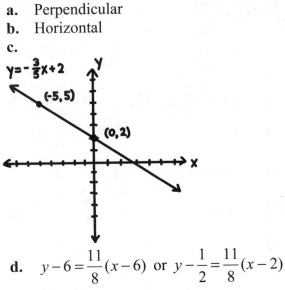

d. $y - 6 = \frac{11}{8}(x - 6)$ or $y - \frac{1}{2} = \frac{11}{8}(x - 2)$

e. 5 hours

Problem Set 76

1. True

2. True

3. $4 + -5i$

4. $-i$

5. $2x^7$

6. $\dfrac{4}{x + 4}$

7. 2

8. $-\dfrac{3}{5}$

9. $\sqrt{5}, -\sqrt{5}$

10. $y = 11x$

x	-2	-1	0	1	2	3
y	-22	-11	0	11	22	33

11. $y = -7x + 2$

x	-2	-1	0	1	2	3
y	16	9	2	-5	-12	-19

12. Parallel

13. Perpendicular

14. Horizontal

15.

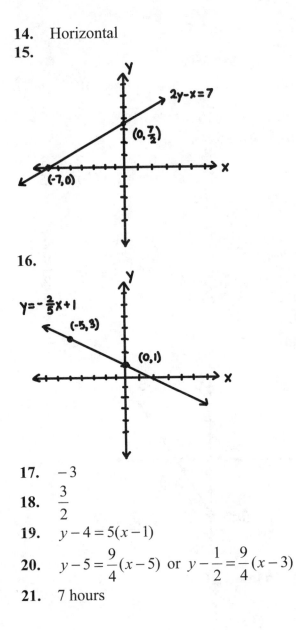

16.

17. -3

18. $\dfrac{3}{2}$

19. $y - 4 = 5(x - 1)$

20. $y - 5 = \frac{9}{4}(x - 5)$ or $y - \frac{1}{2} = \frac{9}{4}(x - 3)$

21. 7 hours

CHAPTER 11

Practice 77

a. $(3x-7)(x-1)$

b. $2x^2+5x+3$

c. -3, -5

d. $y+5=-1(x+4)$ or $y+8=-1(x+1)$

e. 144 seconds

Problem Set 77

1. True
2. True
3. True
4. $-2x(2x+3)$
5. $(3x-5)(x-1)$
6. $-3y^{11}$
7. $3x^2+2x+4$
8. $-\dfrac{6}{11}$
9. $\dfrac{3}{5}$
10. -4, -5
11. $y=7$
12. $y=8$
13. Parallel
14. $y=\dfrac{5x-9}{2}$
15. $y=3x+3$
16. -4
17. 3
18. $y-3=6(x-1)$
19. $y+7=-1(x+6)$ or $y+9=-1(x+4)$
20. 12 hours

Practice 78

a. B

b. $\sqrt{5}i$, $-\sqrt{5}i$, $\sqrt{2}i$, $-\sqrt{2}i$

c. Vertical

d. $y=-\dfrac{5}{2}x+5$

e. $50,000

Problem Set 78

1. True
2. False
3. True
4. C
5. D
6. 9.205×10^6
7. 4.3×10^{-5}
8. $\dfrac{y^{15}}{8}$
9. $\dfrac{2}{x^3}$
10. $\dfrac{10}{23}$
11. 2
12. $\sqrt{3}i$, $-\sqrt{3}i$, $\sqrt{2}i$, $-\sqrt{2}i$
13. $y=\dfrac{1}{2}x+1$

x	-2	-1	0	1	2	3
y	0	$\dfrac{1}{2}$	1	$\dfrac{3}{2}$	2	$\dfrac{5}{2}$

14. $y=x^2$

x	-2	-1	0	1	2	3
y	4	1	0	1	4	9

15. Perpendicular
16. Vertical
17. $\dfrac{2}{3}$
18. -1
19. $y=-\dfrac{1}{8}x+4$
20. $y=-\dfrac{7}{3}x+7$
21. $10

Practice 79

a. $(-2,-6)$

b.

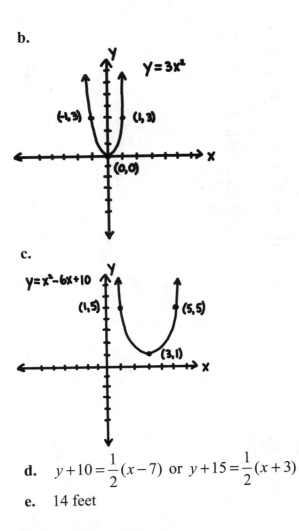

c.

13. $y = 0$

14.

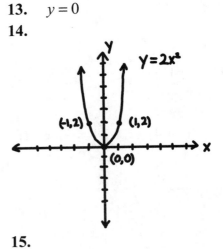

15.

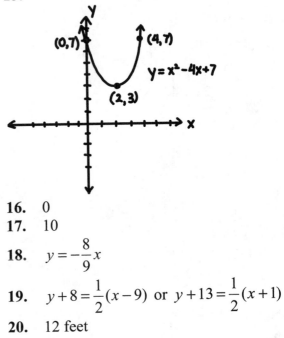

d. $y + 10 = \dfrac{1}{2}(x - 7)$ or $y + 15 = \dfrac{1}{2}(x + 3)$

e. 14 feet

Problem Set 79

1. False
2. True
3. $(0, 0)$
4. $(-1, -1)$
5. $5(1 - 3x^2)$
6. $(x - 8)(x - 3)$
7. $-\dfrac{6}{z^2}$
8. 4
9. $\dfrac{2}{7}$
10. 30
11. $\dfrac{2}{5}$
12. $y = 10$

16. 0

17. 10

18. $y = -\dfrac{8}{9}x$

19. $y + 8 = \dfrac{1}{2}(x - 9)$ or $y + 13 = \dfrac{1}{2}(x + 1)$

20. 12 feet

Practice 80

a. $\dfrac{y - 8}{3y - 1}$

b.

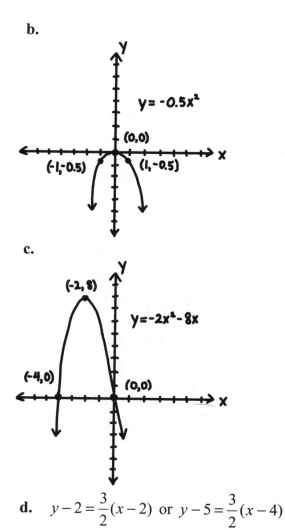

c.

12.

13.

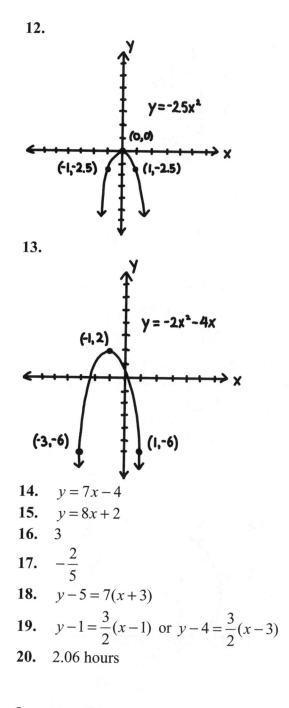

d. $y - 2 = \dfrac{3}{2}(x - 2)$ or $y - 5 = \dfrac{3}{2}(x - 4)$

e. 1.55 hours

Problem Set 80

1. A
2. B
3. -40
4. -15
5. $2x^5 - 10x^4$
6. $\dfrac{y - 7}{3y - 1}$
7. -5
8. $\dfrac{5}{16}$
9. 2, 1
10. $y = -1$
11. $y = -100$

14. $y = 7x - 4$
15. $y = 8x + 2$
16. 3
17. $-\dfrac{2}{5}$
18. $y - 5 = 7(x + 3)$
19. $y - 1 = \dfrac{3}{2}(x - 1)$ or $y - 4 = \dfrac{3}{2}(x - 3)$
20. 2.06 hours

Practice 81

a. Center (5, 4); radius 9

b.

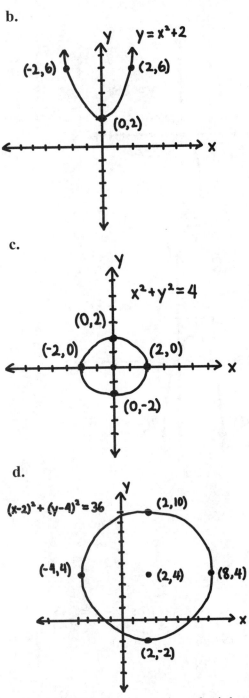

c.

d.

e. 20,000 known species of crickets

4. $(y-9)(y+7)$
5. Vertex $(0, 0)$; opens down
6. Center: $(6, 7)$; radius 12
7. $z^3 + 2z^2 - 2z + 3$
8. $\dfrac{1}{x+3}$
9. 1
10. $\dfrac{6}{5}$
11. 2, 0
12. $y = -23.5$
13. $y = -8$
14.

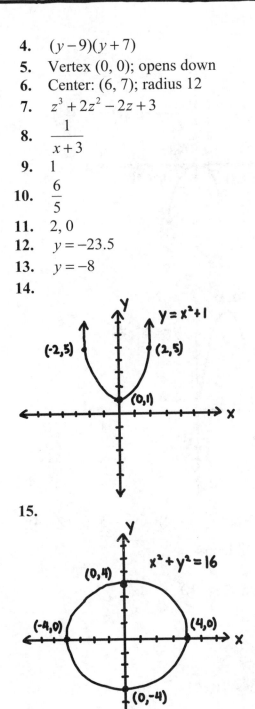

15.

Problem Set 81
1. True
2. True
3. $5x(5x^3 - 1)$

16.

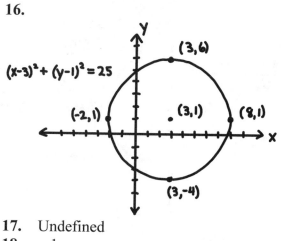

17. Undefined

18. -1

19. $y = 3x - \dfrac{4}{5}$

20. $y + 2 = -2(x-1)$ or $y + 6 = -2(x-3)$

21. 192 people

Practice 82

a. Center (2, 5); radius: 8

b.

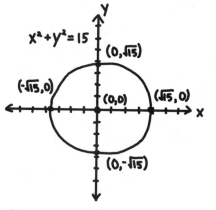

c.

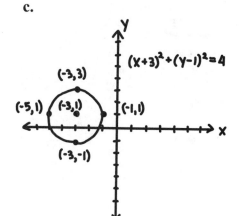

d. $y = \pm\sqrt{64 - x^2}$

e. 325 nickels

Problem Set 82

1. False

2. True

3. Vertex $(9, -4)$; opens up

4. Center (3, 4); radius 7

5. -11

6. 2

7. $-\dfrac{5}{6}x^4 + 3$

8. $\dfrac{x-2}{x^2}$

9. -2

10. 3

11. $-4, -5$

12. $y = 80$

13. $y = 17$

14.

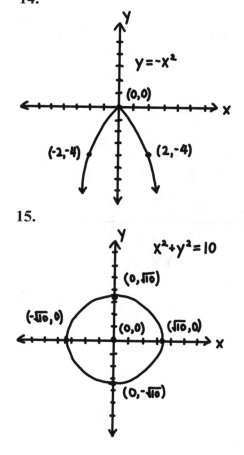

15.

16.

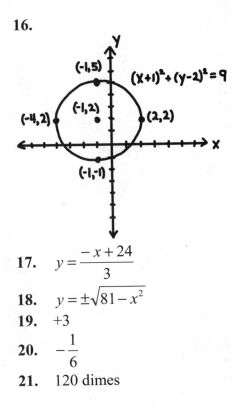

17. $y = \dfrac{-x + 24}{3}$

18. $y = \pm\sqrt{81 - x^2}$

19. $+3$

20. $-\dfrac{1}{6}$

21. 120 dimes

Practice 83

a. Center $(-4,-3)$; radius 4

b. Center $(0,0)$; vertices $(6,0)$, $(-6,0)$

c.

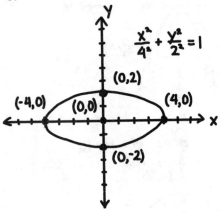

d.

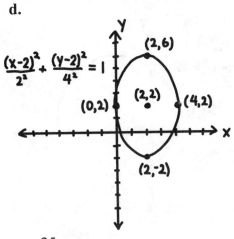

e. 25 ounces

Problem Set 83

1. True

2. True

3. $(x-5)(x-3)$

4. $(2x-3)(x+1)$

5. Center $(-3,-2)$; radius 3

6. Center $(0,0)$; vertices $(5,0)$, $(-5,0)$

7. $\dfrac{y^{15}}{32}$

8. $\dfrac{x-10}{4x}$

9. $\dfrac{6}{7}$

10. $-\dfrac{1}{2}$

11. $-5 + 2i$, $-5 + (-2i)$

12. $y = -2.75$

13. $y = 16$

14.

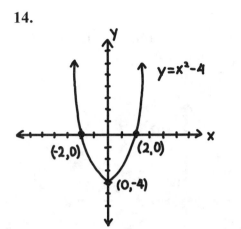

15.

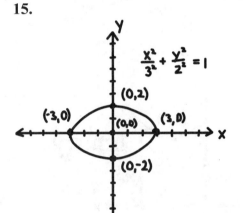

16.

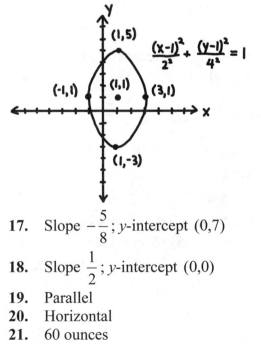

17. Slope $-\dfrac{5}{8}$; y-intercept $(0,7)$

18. Slope $\dfrac{1}{2}$; y-intercept $(0,0)$

19. Parallel

20. Horizontal

21. 60 ounces

Practice 84

a. Vertex $(-2,-5)$; opens up

b. Center $(0,0)$; vertices $(0,5)$, $(0,-5)$

c.

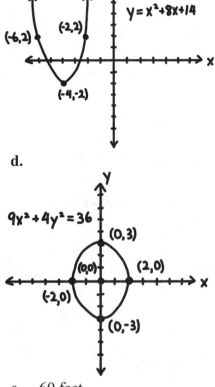

d.

e. 60 feet

Problem Set 84

1. True

2. False

3. Vertex $(-2,-8)$; opens up

4. Center $(7,-1)$; radius 9

5. Center $(0,0)$; vertices $(0,4)$, $(0,-4)$

6. $-10x^9$

7. $\dfrac{5+6x^3}{9x^4}$

8. 1

9. $\sqrt{5}i$, $-\sqrt{5}i$

10. 4 (1 is extraneous)

11. $y=14$

12. $y=13$

13.

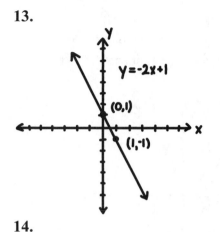

14.

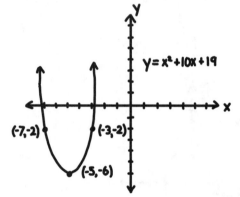

15.

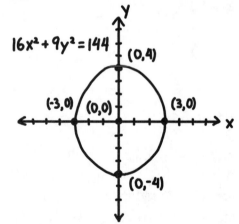

16. $y = -\dfrac{5x}{3}$

17. $y = \pm\sqrt{16 - x^2}$

18. $-\dfrac{2}{3}$

19. -4

20. 100 feet

Practice 85

a. Center $(0,0)$; vertices $(7,0)$, $(-7,0)$; opens left and right

b.

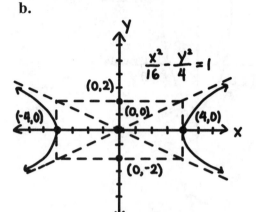

c.

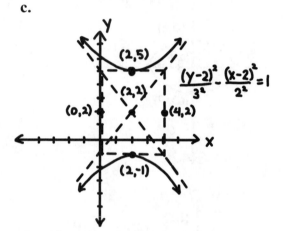

d. Slope 0; y-intercept $(0,-2)$

e. $7,000

Problem Set 85

1. True

2. True

3. $9x(x-3)$

4. $(3x+2)(x+4)$

5. Center $(-3, 9)$; radius $\sqrt{21}$

6. Vertex $(0, 5)$; opens down

7. Center $(0, 0)$; vertices $(5, 0)$, $(-5, 0)$; opens left and right

8. $2y^4 + 5y^3$

9. $\dfrac{3x}{2x+1}$

10. $-\dfrac{1}{2}$

11. 2, 0

12. $y = 8$

13. $y = 2$

14.

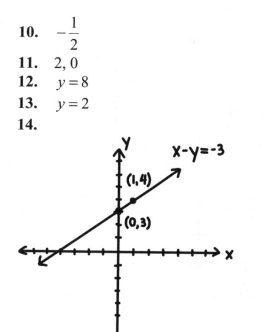

15.

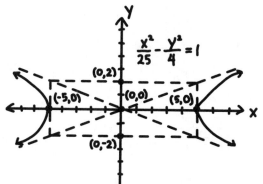

16.

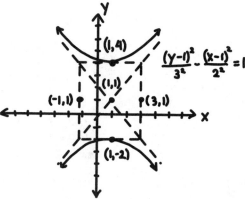

17. Slope 4; y-intercept $(0,-8)$

18. Slope 0; y-intercept $(0,-1)$

19. $y = -\dfrac{1}{4}x + 5$

20. $y + 3 = 2(x - 1)$

21. \$10,000

Practice 86

a. $\sqrt{34}$

b. Center $(2, 3)$; vertices $(2, 7)$, $(2, -1)$; opens up and down

c.

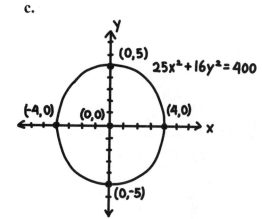

d.

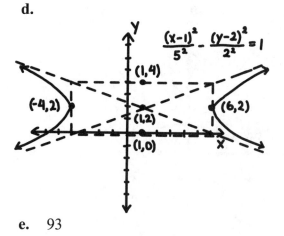

e. 93

Problem Set 86

1. True

2. True

3. $\sqrt{52}$

4. Center $(0, 0)$; radius 10

5. Center $(0, 0)$; vertices $(12, 0)$, $(-12, 0)$

6. Center $(1, 5)$; vertices $(1, 8)$, $(1, 2)$; opens up and down

7. $2x^3 - 7x$

8. $\dfrac{1}{2x - 6}$

9. 3

10. $\dfrac{2}{3}$

11. $y = -80$

12. $y = 2$

13.

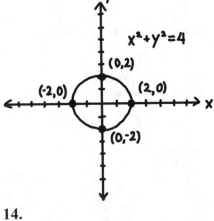

14.

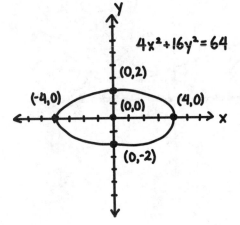

15.

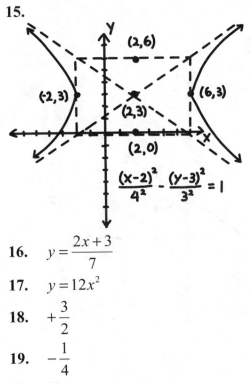

16. $y = \dfrac{2x + 3}{7}$

17. $y = 12x^2$

18. $+\dfrac{3}{2}$

19. $-\dfrac{1}{4}$

20. 91

CHAPTER 12

Practice 87

a. $2\sqrt{17}$

b. Center $(0,0)$; vertices $(\sqrt{11},0)$, $(-\sqrt{11},0)$; opens left and right

c. $A = 25$

d.

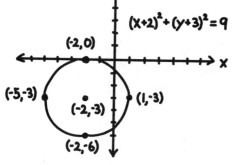

e. 2.5 hours

Problem Set 87

1. True
2. True
3. True
4. $(z-8)(z+3)$
5. $(x-2)(x-1)$
6. $4\sqrt{5}$
7. Vertex $(0,0)$; opens up
8. Center $(11,12)$; radius 5
9. Center $(0,0)$; vertices $(\sqrt{5},0)$, $(-\sqrt{5},0)$; opens left and right
10. $x^3 - x^2 - 7x + 3$
11. $\dfrac{x-8}{x+5}$
12. -1
13. $3, 0$
14. $y = -137$
15. $A = 24$

16.

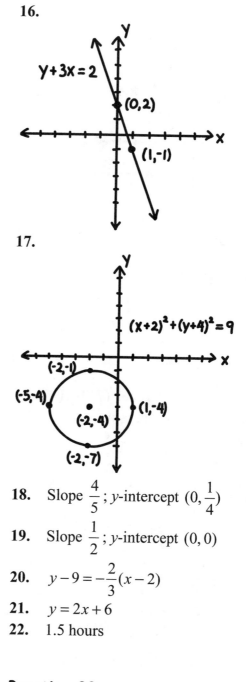

17.

18. Slope $\dfrac{4}{5}$; y-intercept $(0,\dfrac{1}{4})$

19. Slope $\dfrac{1}{2}$; y-intercept $(0,0)$

20. $y - 9 = -\dfrac{2}{3}(x-2)$

21. $y = 2x + 6$

22. 1.5 hours

Practice 88

a. Vertex $(-1,3)$; opens up

b. $f = \dfrac{h}{et}$

c. $e = \dfrac{j}{1+ft}$

d.

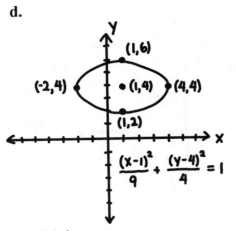

$$\frac{(x-1)^2}{9} + \frac{(y-4)^2}{4} = 1$$

e. 24 degrees

Problem Set 88

1. False
2. True
3. 0
4. -1
5. $\sqrt{85}$
6. Center $(0,0)$; vertices $(7,0)$, $(-7,0)$
7. Vertex $(-1,4)$; opens up
8. $-64x^{10}$
9. $\dfrac{3x+6}{2x^4+14x^3}$
10. $\dfrac{96}{7}$
11. $9, -4$
12. $V = 320$
13. $z = 30$
14. $r = \dfrac{i}{pt}$
15. $p = \dfrac{A}{1+rt}$

16.

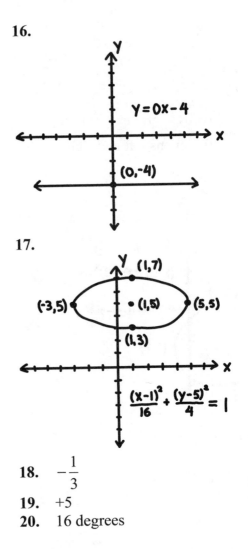

17.

$$\frac{(x-1)^2}{16} + \frac{(y-5)^2}{4} = 1$$

18. $-\dfrac{1}{3}$
19. $+5$
20. 16 degrees

Practice 89

a. Center $(-3,-6)$; vertices $(-3,-3)$, $(-3,-9)$; opens up and down

b. $x = \dfrac{\pm\sqrt{y}}{5}$

c. $m = -\dfrac{d}{c-1}$ or $m = \dfrac{d}{1-c}$

d.

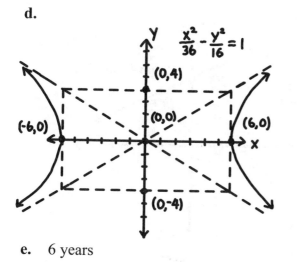

e. 6 years

Problem Set 89

1. 256
2. $-21 + (-i)$
3. $6(3 - 4y^2)$
4. $(3x + 5)(x - 4)$
5. 5
6. Center $(0, 0)$; radius $\sqrt{17}$
7. Center $(-4, -8)$; vertices $(-4, -4)$, $(-4, -12)$; opens up and down
8. $-20x^5 + 12x^4$
9. $\dfrac{7y + 6}{12y^2}$
10. -8
11. $\dfrac{7}{3}$
12. $\dfrac{23}{5}$
13. $w = -13$
14. $d = -144$
15. $t = \dfrac{\pm\sqrt{d}}{4}$
16. $n = -\dfrac{b}{a - 1}$ or $n = \dfrac{b}{1 - a}$

17.

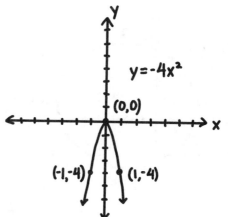

18.

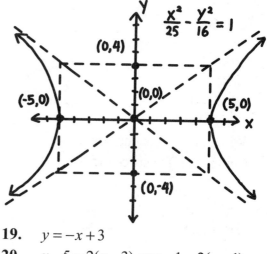

19. $y = -x + 3$
20. $y - 5 = 2(x - 3)$ or $y - 1 = 2(x - 1)$
21. 5 years

Practice 90

a. Center $(1, 3)$; vertices $(5, 3)$; $(-3, 3)$
b. $y = \dfrac{dg}{d - e}$
c. $g = \dfrac{cd}{c + d}$

d.

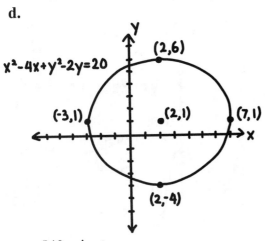

$x^2-4x+y^2-2y=20$

(2,6), (-3,1), (2,1), (7,1), (2,-4)

e. 540 minutes

Problem Set 90

1. True
2. True
3. False
4. 1.653×10^{19}
5. 6×10^3
6. Vertex $(0,0)$; opens down
7. Center $(2,1)$; vertices $(5,1)$, $(-1,1)$
8. $\dfrac{2}{x^5}$
9. $\dfrac{3x^3 + 12x^2}{4}$
10. 9
11. $5i, \ -5i$
12. 8 (2 is extraneous)
13. $L = -36$
14. $s = -2$
15. $x = \dfrac{ac}{a-b}$
16. $f = \dfrac{ab}{a+b}$

17.

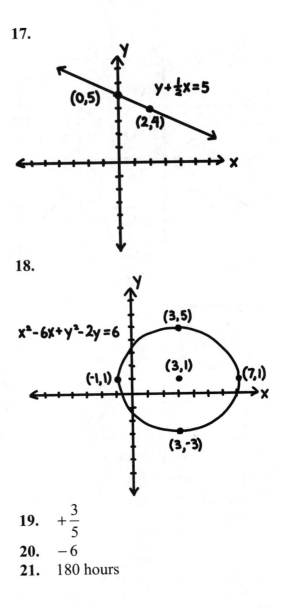

(0,5), (2,4), $y + \frac{1}{2}x = 5$

18.

$x^2-6x+y^2-2y=6$

(3,5), (-1,1), (3,1), (7,1), (3,-3)

19. $+\dfrac{3}{5}$
20. -6
21. 180 hours

Practice 91

a. Center $(0,0)$; vertices $(5,0)$, $(-5,0)$; opens left and right
b. $v = \dfrac{t - 2u}{2}$
c. $y = \dfrac{e}{c+d}$

d.

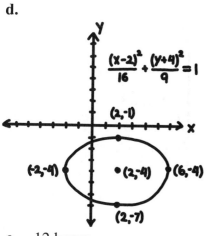

e. 12 hours

Problem Set 91

1. True
2. True
3. $6 + (-10i)$
4. 16
5. $\sqrt{58}$
6. Center $(4, 2)$; radius 11
7. Center $(0, 0)$; vertices $(7, 0)$, $(-7, 0)$; opens left and right
8. $-16x^3 + 9x$
9. $\dfrac{9}{x^4}$
10. 2
11. -7
12. -2, -4
13. $H = -21$
14. $z = 20$
15. $l = \dfrac{p - 2w}{2}$
16. $x = \dfrac{c}{a + b}$

17.

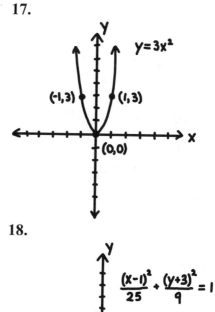

18.

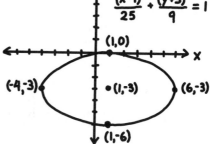

19. $y = 2x$
20. $y - 0 = -\dfrac{1}{3}(x + 2)$ or $y - 1 = -\dfrac{1}{3}(x + 5)$
21. 15 hours

Practice 92

a. Vertex $(-4, -23)$; opens up
b. Center $(0, 0)$; vertices $(5, 0)$, $(-5, 0)$
c. $w = \dfrac{k + l}{z}$

d.

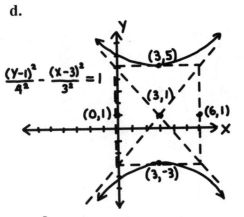

$$\frac{(y-1)^2}{4^2} - \frac{(x-3)^2}{3^2} = 1$$

(3,5) (3,1) (0,1) (6,1) (3,-3)

e. 8 quarters

Problem Set 92

1. True
2. True
3. False
4. -44
5. 2
6. Vertex $(-3, -15)$; opens up
7. Center $(0, 0)$; vertices $(6, 0)$, $(-6, 0)$
8. $x^2 - 7x + 12$
9. $\dfrac{2}{y - 7}$
10. 8
11. 3
12. $-1, -10$
13. $d = 144$
14. $h = \dfrac{3V}{ab}$
15. $y = \dfrac{h + j}{x}$

16.

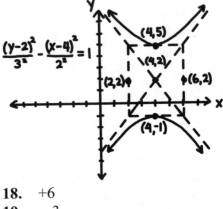

$3x - y = 1$ (1,2)   (0,-1)

17.

$$\frac{(y-2)^2}{3^2} - \frac{(x-4)^2}{2^2} = 1$$

(4,5) (4,2) (2,2) (6,2) (4,-1)

18. $+6$
19. -3
20. 11 nickels

CHAPTER 13

Practice 93

a. Center $(-3, -4)$; radius $\sqrt{21}$

b. $8x^2y^7z^3$

c. $J = \dfrac{f}{d-e}$

d. $x = 3$ or $x + 0y = 3$

e. 14

Problem Set 93

1. True
2. False
3. 3.8×10^{10}
4. 1.95×10^{-3}
5. $\sqrt{61}$
6. Parallel
7. Center $(-1, -8)$; radius $\sqrt{19}$
8. $8x^2y^2$
9. $\dfrac{-2x+13}{20x^4}$
10. $5x^3y^4z^2$
11. $9x^4y^{12}z^2$
12. 9
13. 5
14. $-7 + \sqrt{10}i$, $-7 + (-\sqrt{10}i)$
15. $z = -33$
16. $x = \dfrac{z - by}{a}$
17. $R = \dfrac{c}{a-b}$

18.

19.

20. $y + 1 = 6(x+1)$
21. $x = 2$ or $x + 0y = 2$
22. 18

Practice 94

a. $10x^5y^4z^2 - 12x^5y^{10}z$

b. $x^4 + 7x^3y + 14x^2y^2 + 7xy^3 + y^4$

c. $r = -\dfrac{qs}{q-s}$ or $r = \dfrac{qs}{s-q}$

d.

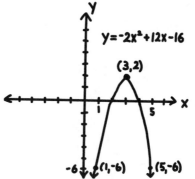

e.   988 lefties

Problem Set 94

1. $3 + 5i$
2. $23 + 11i$
3. Perpendicular
4. Horizontal
5. Center $(0, 0)$; vertices $(9, 0)$, $(-9, 0)$
6. $-14t^4u^3$
7. $8x^3y^3z - 10x^5y^6z^2$
8. $\dfrac{7}{12}x^2y^4z^2$
9. $x^3 - 3x^2y + 3xy^2 - y^3$
10. $x^4 + 3x^3y + 4x^2y^2 + 3xy^3 + y^4$
11. $\dfrac{4}{7}$
12. $\dfrac{5}{11}$
13. $2, 0$
14. $f = 9$
15. $a = \dfrac{bc}{b - c}$
16.

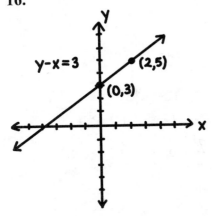

17.

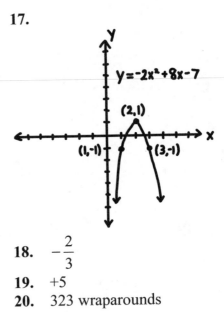

18. $-\dfrac{2}{3}$
19. $+5$
20. 323 wraparounds

Practice 95

a. $(x + z)(p + q)$
b. $-3x^4y^2z(3xz^2 + 4y)$
c. $(f + g)(5q - 7p)$
d. $v = \dfrac{e^2 + f}{d + e}$
e. 1.5 pounds

Problem Set 95

1. True
2. True
3. 1.675×10^{-8}
4. 3.4×10^{-6}
5. $\sqrt{13}$
6. Vertical
7. Center $(0, 0)$; radius $\sqrt{31}$
8. $2x^2yz(xy + 5z^2)$
9. $(x + y)(a + b)$
10. $-2x^3y^5z(3xz + 4y^2)$
11. $(h + k)(3m - 2n)$
12. $5p^3m^6$
13. $-12x^3y^4 + 21x^2y^5$
14. $a^3 + 4a^2b + 4ab^2 + b^3$

15. $16x^{12}y^{16}z^{28}$

16. $\dfrac{17}{4}$

17. $\sqrt{7}$, $-\sqrt{7}$

18. $z = 52$

19. $t = \dfrac{c + b^2}{a + b}$

20. $y - 0 = -4(x - 3)$ or $y - 4 = -4(x - 2)$

21. $y - 2 = \dfrac{3}{4}(x + 1)$ or $y + 1 = \dfrac{3}{4}(x + 5)$

22. 4.8 ounces

Practice 96

a. $(a + b)(a + b)$

b. $(x + 3a)(x + 4a)$

c. $(a - b)(7y + 3t)$

d. $g = \dfrac{JG - JE + ej}{j}$

e. $1.20

Problem Set 96

1. -6
2. 21
3. Parallel
4. Vertex $(0, 0)$; opens down
5. Center $(0, 0)$; vertices $(0, 5)$, $(0, -5)$; opens up and down
6. $8x^3y^3(x^2 - 2y)$
7. $(x + y)(x + y)$
8. $(x + 3a)(x + 2a)$
9. $(a - b)(9x + 2r)$
10. $\dfrac{1}{6}r^2t^5$
11. $10a^4b^3 + 5a^6b^3$
12. $x^2 + 3xy + 2y^2$
13. -4
14. -1
15. $\sqrt{6}i$, $-\sqrt{6}i$
16. $f = 38$

17. $f = \dfrac{MF - MI + mi}{m}$

18.

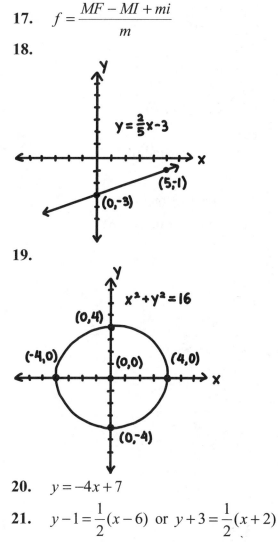

19.

20. $y = -4x + 7$

21. $y - 1 = \dfrac{1}{2}(x - 6)$ or $y + 3 = \dfrac{1}{2}(x + 2)$

22. $1

Practice 97

a. $(x + b)(x + b)$ or $(x + b)^2$

b. $(y - a)(y - a)$ or $(y - a)^2$

c. $r^2 - 2rt + t^2$

d. $l = \pm\sqrt{\dfrac{km - Fr^2}{F}}$

e. 1.63 hours

Problem Set 97

1. True
2. True
3. 2.9106×10^7
4. 5×10^{-9}
5. $\sqrt{61}$
6. Horizontal
7. Center $(9, 4)$; radius 5
8. $5x^2 y^2 (xy - 2)$
9. $(x + c)(x + c)$ or $(x + c)^2$
10. $(y - b)(y - b)$ or $(y - b)^2$
11. $18x^5 y^8 z^3$
12. $16a^{10} b^4 c^6$
13. $x^2 + 2xy + y^2$
14. $p^2 - 2pq + q^2$
15. $-\dfrac{8}{5}$
16. 4
17. $S = 125.6$
18. $h = \pm\sqrt{\dfrac{kq - Er^2}{E}}$
19. $-\dfrac{1}{2}$
20. $\dfrac{1}{3}$
21. 2.08 hours

Practice 98

a. $(8c^2 + 5d)(8c^2 - 5d)$
b. $(x - 6b)(x - 2b)$
c. $u = \pm\sqrt{\dfrac{5.6t^2}{2s}}$

d.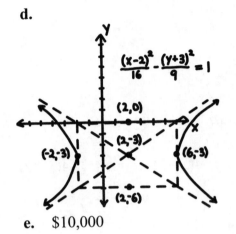
$$\frac{(x-2)^2}{16} - \frac{(y+3)^2}{9} = 1$$

e. $10,000

Problem Set 98

1. $64i$
2. $-16 + (-18i)$
3. Perpendicular
4. Center $(0, 0)$; vertices $(8, 0)$, $(-8, 0)$
5. $(x + y)(x - y)$
6. $(x - y)(x - y)$ or $(x - y)^2$
7. $(9a^2 + 7b)(9a^2 - 7b)$
8. $3pq(1 - 2pq)$
9. $(x - 5b)(x - 2b)$
10. $4x^3 y + 3x^2 y^2$
11. $x^2 - y^2$
12. $r^3 + 3r^2 s + 3rs^2 + s^3$
13. $5xyz + 5y$
14. $-\dfrac{5}{3}$
15. $0, -4$
16. $p = 30$
17. $v = \pm\sqrt{\dfrac{9.8x^2}{2y}}$

18.

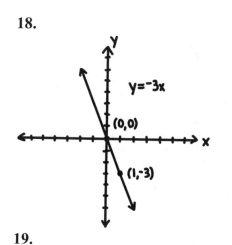

19.

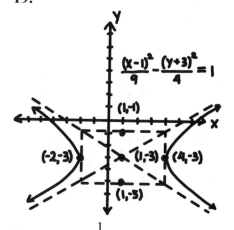

20. $y + 5 = \dfrac{1}{6}(x + 4)$

21. $y = \dfrac{3}{2}x + 1$

22. \$20,000

Practice 99

a. $(4gh + 9kp)(4gh - 9kp)$

b. $\dfrac{c}{6dx}$

c. $\dfrac{ay + by}{ab - b^2}$

d. $\dfrac{1}{63xy}$

e. 50 feet

Problem Set 99

1. 2.548×10^{18}

2. 2.1×10^5

3. 5

4. Vertical

5. Vertex $(8, 3)$; opens up

6. $8xy(y^2 + 7x)$

7. $(y + z)(y + z)$ or $(y + z)^2$

8. $(3pq + 10st)(3pq - 10st)$

9. $\dfrac{b}{5ax}$

10. $\dfrac{ab + c}{2d}$

11. $\dfrac{8}{27}x^{15}y^{12}$

12. $\dfrac{x^2 + xy}{bx - by}$

13. $\dfrac{4}{7}xyz$

14. $\dfrac{1}{15t}$

15. 28

16. $-1, -3$

17. $y = -10$

18. $s = \dfrac{uv - t}{2}$

19. $y = 4x + 2$

20. $y + 2 = -\dfrac{3}{7}(x - 2)$ or

$y - 1 = -\dfrac{3}{7}(x + 5)$

21. 140 feet

Practice 100

a. $(x + 4)(x - 4)$

b. $\dfrac{x - y}{x + y}$

c. $\dfrac{-4ab}{a^2 - b^2}$ or $\dfrac{4ab}{b^2 - a^2}$

d. $w = \dfrac{a - bc}{c - 1}$

e. 1.25 hours

Problem Set 100

1. 24
2. -1
3. Parallel
4. Center $(-7, 2)$; radius 10
5. $xyz(x^2 - yz)$
6. $(x + 5)(x - 5)$
7. $(x - y)(x - y)$ or $(x - y)^2$
8. $27abx^5y^8z^3$
9. $u^2 + 2uv + v^2$
10. $\dfrac{bx^2}{x - a}$
11. $\dfrac{3y^2}{10}$
12. $\dfrac{a - b}{a + b}$
13. $-\dfrac{4rs}{r^2 - s^2}$ or $\dfrac{4rs}{s^2 - r^2}$
14. 2
15. 8
16. $z = 4$
17. $m = \dfrac{x - zy}{z - 1}$
18.

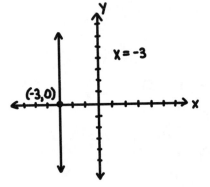

19.

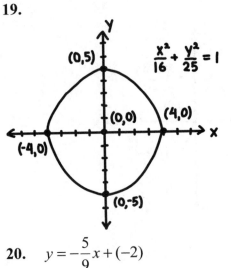

20. $y = -\dfrac{5}{9}x + (-2)$
21. $y + 4 = -2(x - 1)$ or $y + 6 = -2(x - 2)$
22. 1.75 hours

Practice 101

a. $(5xy + 6q^2p^2)(5xy - 6q^2p^2)$
b. $16a^2b^2 - 25c^2d^2$
c. $\dfrac{1}{x + 2b}$
d. $2x^2 + 5xy + y^2$
e. 15 degrees

Problem Set 101

1. 7.95×10^8
2. 3.2×10^{-10}
3. $\sqrt{10}$
4. Horizontal
5. Center $(0, 0)$; vertices $(4, 0)$, $(-4, 0)$; opens left and right
6. $5xy^2z^2(xy + 3z)$
7. $(a + b)(a + b)$ or $(a + b)^2$
8. $(2rt + 3u^2v^2)(2rt - 3u^2v^2)$
9. $-4p^2qr^4$
10. $49x^2y^2 - 16p^2q^2$
11. $\dfrac{b}{x - a}$

12. $\dfrac{1}{x^2 + xy}$

13. $\dfrac{1}{x + 5b}$

14. $2x^2 + 4xy + y^2$

15. -3

16. 5 (2 is extraneous)

17. $u = 144$

18. $y = x$

19. $y - 3 = -\dfrac{1}{2}(x - 2)$ or

    $y - 2 = -\dfrac{1}{2}(x - 4)$

20. $y - 0 = 3(x + 4)$ or $y + 3 = 3(x + 5)$

21. 12 degrees

CHAPTER 14

Practice 102

a. $(x-y)(cd+r)$

b. $\dfrac{u+v}{v}$

c. $x=3$, $y=2$

d. $x=7$, $y=-2$

e. 1.2 hours

Problem Set 102

1. True
2. True
3. $-38+(-16i)$
4. 125
5. Parallel
6. Center $(0,0)$; radius $\sqrt{7}$
7. $(y-b)(y-b)$ or $(y-b)^2$
8. $(x-y)(ab+p)$
9. $(jx+ky)(jx-ky)$
10. $26x^5y^5z^5$
11. $u^2+2ut+t^2$
12. $\dfrac{ax+ay}{bx-by}$
13. $\dfrac{x+y}{y}$
14. $\dfrac{11}{2}$
15. $2i$, $-2i$
16. $z=1$
17. $d=\dfrac{g+ef}{s}$

18.

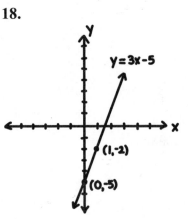

19.

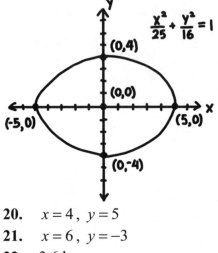

20. $x=4$, $y=5$
21. $x=6$, $y=-3$
22. 3.6 hours

Practice 103

a. $\dfrac{u-v}{uv}$

b. $f=-\dfrac{bn}{h-n}$ or $f=\dfrac{bn}{n-h}$

c. $x=-4$, $y=1$

d. $x=1$, $y=1$

e. 12 years old

Problem Set 103

1. 85
2. -4
3. $5\sqrt{2}$
4. Vertex $(0,0)$; opens down

5. $ab(x^2 + y^5)$

6. $(p+q)(p+q)$ or $(p+q)^2$

7. $(9cv + 7d^2u^2)(9cv - 7d^2u^2)$

8. $8.8m^2n$

9. $x^3 - 3x^2y + 3xy^2 - y^3$

10. $\dfrac{2ab + 2b^2}{a}$

11. $\dfrac{x - y}{xy}$

12. $x^2 - 4xy + y^2$

13. 12

14. $\sqrt{10}\,,\ -\sqrt{10}$

15. $Q = 45$

16. $k = -\dfrac{al}{j-l}$ or $k = \dfrac{al}{l-j}$

17. $y + 4 = 6(x + 9)$

18. $y + 2 = -1(x - 1)$ or $y - 2 = -1(x + 3)$

19. $x = 21$, $y = 28$

20. $x = -5$, $y = 1$

21. $x = 1$, $y = -1$

22. 20 years old

Practice 104

a. $(x - 3a)(x - a)$

b. $h = \dfrac{a - bj}{1 - j}$

c.

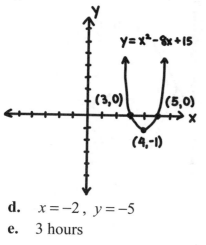

d. $x = -2$, $y = -5$

e. 3 hours

Problem Set 104

1. False

2. True

3. 2.736×10^{-7}

4. 5.625×10^5

5. Perpendicular

6. Center $(0,0)$; vertices $(7,0)$ $(-7,0)$

7. $(r + s)(r - s)$

8. $(x - 2a)(x - a)$

9. $-27x^{12}y^6z^{15}$

10. $e^2 - 2ef + f^2$

11. $\dfrac{b^2 - a^2}{a^2b^2}$

12. $\dfrac{3x + 3y}{4x}$

13. -19

14. $\dfrac{13}{2}$

15. $F = 292.8$

16. $y = \dfrac{a - bx}{1 - x}$

17.

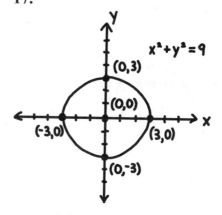

18.

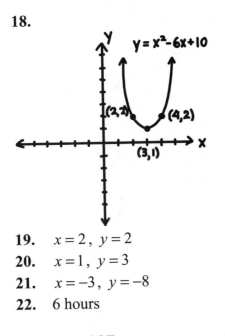

19. $x = 2$, $y = 2$
20. $x = 1$, $y = 3$
21. $x = -3$, $y = -8$
22. 6 hours

Practice 105

a. $(4a^3b^3 + 5x^3y^3)(4a^3b^3 - 5x^3y^3)$

b. $x = \dfrac{1}{2}$, $y = 3$

c. $x = 2$, $y = 1$

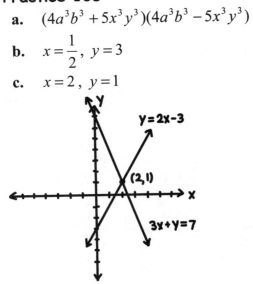

d. No solutions

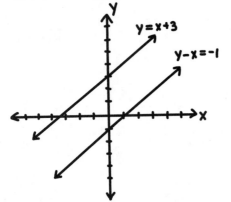

e. 9, 15

Problem Set 105

1. True
2. True
3. 5×10^9
4. 4.73×10^{-5}
5. $\sqrt{41}$
6. Center $(5, 4)$; radius 9
7. $xyz(1 + xyz)$
8. $(y - z)(y - z)$ or $(y - z)^2$
9. $(2g^3h^3 + 3j^3k^3)(2g^3h^3 - 3j^3k^3)$
10. $\dfrac{1}{2}x^4y^5$
11. $j^2 + 2jk + k^2$
12. $\dfrac{x + a}{x}$
13. $\dfrac{x^2 + 2y^2}{10x^2y^2}$
14. 7
15. $0, -5$
16. $A = 40$
17. $s = \dfrac{av}{tv - 1}$
18. $x = 1$, $y = 4$
19. $x = \dfrac{1}{3}$, $y = -2$
20. $x = 1$, $y = 1$

21. No solutions

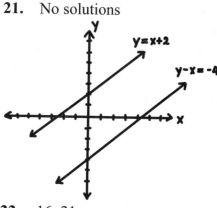

22. 16, 21

Practice 106

a. Center $(0,0)$; vertices $(0,3)$, $(0,-3)$; opens up and down

b. Yes

c. $x=2$, $y=6$

d. Infinite solutions

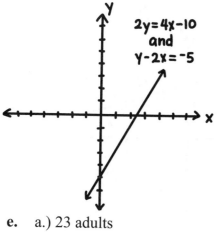

e. a.) 23 adults
b.) 14 children

Problem Set 106

1. $26i$

2. $-18+8i$

3. Vertical

4. Center $(0,0)$; vertices $(0,2)$, $(0,-2)$; opens up and down

5. $7a^2b(2+ab)$

6. $(u+v)(u+v)$ or $(u+v)^2$

7. $(2x+3y)(2x-3y)$

8. $-14g^7h^6$

9. $\dfrac{x-y}{xy^2}$

10. $\dfrac{c+d}{c^3d}$

11. Yes

12. Yes

13. $\dfrac{3}{25}$

14. 5

15. $p=68$

16. $M=\dfrac{ar^2}{G}$

17. $x=3$, $y=7$

18. $x=-2$, $y=-3$

19. No solutions

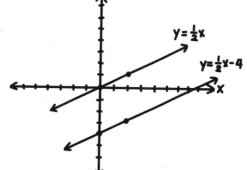

20. Infinite solutions

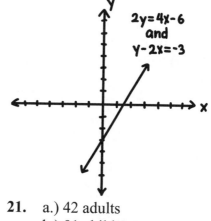

21. a.) 42 adults
b.) 91 children

Practice 107

a. Vertex $(0, 2)$; opens up

b. $x^2 - 3xy + y^2$

c. $x = 2$, $y = 5$

d. Four solution pairs

e. 30 quarters

Problem Set 107

1. True
2. False
3. -2
4. 9
5. $\sqrt{34}$
6. Vertex $(0, 4)$; opens up
7. $-6xy(y + 2x)$
8. $(r - s)(r - s)$ or $(r - s)^2$
9. $x + 9y$
10. $16u^2 - 25t^2$
11. $x^2 - 2xy + y^2$
12. $\dfrac{4}{3}$
13. $\dfrac{8}{3}$
14. 7, 3
15. $y = 4x - 2$
16. $y + 2 = -1(x + 2)$ or $y - 1 = -1(x + 5)$
17. $x = 5$, $y = -1$
18. $x = 1$, $y = 3$
19. Two solution pairs
20. Four solution pairs
21. 60 dimes

Practice 108

a. $q = \dfrac{h}{f^2 + gh}$

b. $x = 3$, $y = 3$

c. $x = 3$, $y = 9$ and $x = 1$, $y = 1$

d. $x = -4$, $y = -18$ and $x = -1$, $y = -3$

e. 29, 8

Problem Set 108

1. Parallel
2. Center $(1, -3)$; radius 4
3. $bx^2 y^3 (y + ax)$
4. $(a + b)(a + b)$ or $(a + b)^2$
5. $(p + q)(m + n)$
6. $\dfrac{36}{x^4 y^6}$
7. $x^3 - x^2 z - xz^2 + z^3$
8. $\dfrac{xy}{x^2 - y^2}$
9. Yes
10. No
11. -2
12. $0, -7$
13. $y = 48$
14. $p = \dfrac{c}{a^2 + bc}$
15.

16.

17. $x = 9$, $y = 0$
18. $x = 2$, $y = 2$
19. $x = 2$, $y = 4$ and $x = 1$, $y = 1$
20. $x = -2$, $y = -1$ and $x = -1$, $y = 1$
21. $42, 68$

19. $x = 4$, $y = 6$ and $x = -4$, $y = 6$ and
    $x = 4$, $y = -6$ and $x = -4$, $y = -6$
20. a.) \$30 for each pair of sneakers
    b.) \$35 for each pair of pants

Practice 109

a. Center $(1, 3)$; vertices $(7, 3)$, $(-5, 3)$
b. $\dfrac{t^2}{r^2}$
c. $x = 5$, $y = -20$ and $x = 1$, $y = -4$
d. $x = 7$, $y = 5$ and $x = -7$, $y = 5$ and
   $x = 7$, $y = -5$ and $x = -7$, $y = -5$
e. a.) \$16 for each butterfly net
   b.) \$18 for each magnifying glass

Practice 110

a. $t = \dfrac{y}{k}$
b. $x = 3$, $y = 18$ and $x = -1.5$, $y = 4.5$
c. $x = 6$, $y = 8$ and $x = -6$, $y = -8$
d. $x = 3$, $y = 1$, $z = 2$
e. 25 ounces

Problem Set 110

1. True
2. False
3. $ax^3 y^5 (x - y)$
4. $(y - 5a)(y + 2a)$
5. $4p^4 q^2$
6. $4f^2 + 12fg + 9g^2$
7. $\dfrac{x + y}{2x^2 - 2xy}$
8. $a^2 c - b^2 c$
9. $\dfrac{3}{4}$
10. 2
11. $w = -35$
12. $t = \dfrac{x}{c}$
13.

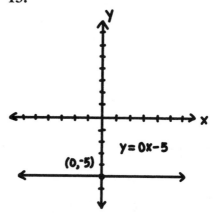

Problem Set 109

1. 1.512×10^{17}
2. 5×10^{-4}
3. $\sqrt{13}$
4. Center $(1, 2)$; vertices $(9, 2)$, $(-7, 2)$
5. $3rt(1 + 3r)$
6. $(x + y)(x + y)$
7. $(u + v)(u - v)$
8. $20a^7 b^7 c^3$
9. $\dfrac{2}{x + 2}$
10. $\dfrac{y^2}{x^2}$
11. $\dfrac{yz}{3x}$
12. -3
13. $\sqrt{5}i + 2$, $-\sqrt{5}i + 2$
14. $d = 156.8$
15. $I = \dfrac{Bc}{4\pi N}$
16. $x = -1$, $y = -8$
17. $x = 4$, $y = 5$
18. $x = 5$, $y = -30$ and $x = 1$, $y = -6$

14.

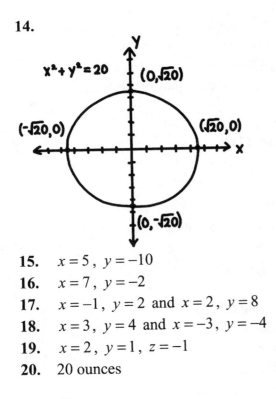

$x^2 + y^2 = 20$

$(0, \sqrt{20})$

$(-\sqrt{20}, 0)$

$(\sqrt{20}, 0)$

$(0, -\sqrt{20})$

15. $x = 5$, $y = -10$
16. $x = 7$, $y = -2$
17. $x = -1$, $y = 2$ and $x = 2$, $y = 8$
18. $x = 3$, $y = 4$ and $x = -3$, $y = -4$
19. $x = 2$, $y = 1$, $z = -1$
20. 20 ounces

9. $-\dfrac{16}{3}$
10. $\sqrt{2}i + 5$, $-\sqrt{2}i + 5$
11. $z = -7$
12. $c = \dfrac{f}{d - e}$
13. $y - 3 = -\dfrac{1}{4}(x - 1)$
14. $y - 0 = -2(x - 1)$ or $y - 6 = -2(x + 2)$
15. $x = \dfrac{1}{3}$, $y = 4$
16. $x = -5$, $y = -11$
17. $x = -6$, $y = -3$ and $x = -1$, $y = 2$
18. $x = 2$, $y = 3$ and $x = -2$, $y = 3$ and $x = 2$, $y = -3$ and $x = -2$, $y = -3$
19. $a = 1$, $b = 3$, $c = -1$
20. 16, 54

Practice 111

a. $g = \dfrac{l}{h - k}$
b. $x = -8$, $y = -4$ and $x = -1$, $y = 3$
c. $x = 3$, $y = 4$ and $x = -3$, $y = 4$ and $x = 3$, $y = -4$ and $x = -3$, $y = -4$
d. $a = 2$, $b = 2$, $c = -3$
e. 13, 42

Problem Set 111

1. 5.893×10^{7}
2. 1.8×10^{-3}
3. $\dfrac{1}{25h^4 j^6 k^8}$
4. $\dfrac{x + a}{x - 3a}$
5. $\dfrac{x^2 + y^2}{x^2 - y^2}$
6. $-\dfrac{x + 7}{7xy}$ or $\dfrac{-x - 7}{7xy}$
7. No
8. Yes

CHAPTER 15

Practice 112

a. $x = 0$, $y = -3$ and $x = \sqrt{5}$, $y = 2$ and $x = -\sqrt{5}$, $y = 2$

b. $x = -5$, $y = 2$, $z = 4$

c. All of the numbers greater than or equal to -6

d. $x \geq -2$

![number line with closed dot at -2, shaded to the right from -5 to 6]

e. 18 feet

Problem Set 112

1. True
2. False
3. $(y + a)(y + a)$ or $(y + a)^2$
4. $(3st + 4uv)(3st - 4uv)$
5. $-70x^6 y^8$
6. $2x^3 + 10xy + x^2 y + 5y^2$
7. $\dfrac{3xy}{x - y}$
8. $\dfrac{a + b}{2}$
9. -8
10. 6, 2
11. $-\dfrac{5}{12}$
12. $r = \dfrac{vw}{s + t}$
13. No solutions
14. $x = 2$, $y = 1$
15. $x = 0$, $y = -5$ and $x = 3$, $y = 4$ and $x = -3$, $y = 4$
16. $x = -4$, $y = 1$, $z = 3$
17. All of the numbers less than 15
18. All of the numbers greater than or equal to -9
19. $x < 4$

![number line with open dot at 4, shaded to the left, from -5 to 6]

20. $x \geq -5$

![number line with closed dot at -5, shaded to the right, from -5 to 6]

21. 24 feet

Practice 113

a. $x = 5$, $y = 20$ and $x = -1$, $y = -4$

b. $x = 3$, $y = 4$, $z = 5$

c. $x \geq -4$

d. $x \geq 56$

e. a.) \$4 for each duct tape
b.) \$30 for each radio

Problem Set 113

1. True
2. True
3. $22 + (-14i)$
4. $-27i$
5. $6xy - y$
6. $8x + 7y$
7. $\dfrac{2b}{3a^2}$
8. 14
9. 6
10. $y = 11x + 15$
11. $y - 3 = \dfrac{7}{9}(x - 2)$ or $y + 4 = \dfrac{7}{9}(x + 7)$
12.

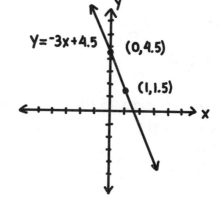

67

13.

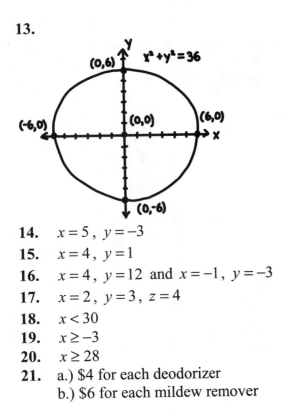

14. $x = 5$, $y = -3$

15. $x = 4$, $y = 1$

16. $x = 4$, $y = 12$ and $x = -1$, $y = -3$

17. $x = 2$, $y = 3$, $z = 4$

18. $x < 30$

19. $x \geq -3$

20. $x \geq 28$

21. a.) \$4 for each deodorizer

b.) \$6 for each mildew remover

Practice 114

a. $t = \dfrac{s + u}{s - 1}$

b. $x = 4$, $y = 2$ and $x = -4$, $y = 2$ and $x = 4$, $y = -2$ and $x = -4$, $y = -2$

c. $x = 2$, $y = 1$, $z = 1$

d. $x > 3$

e. 1,426 late-sleepers

Problem Set 114

1. $\sqrt{117}$

2. Center $(0, 0)$; vertices $(5, 0)$, $(-5, 0)$; opens left and right

3. $8xy(y + 3x)$

4. $(j + k)(2a + 3b)$

5. $\dfrac{49}{x^4 y^8 z^6}$

6. $\dfrac{a + b}{c}$

7. $-\dfrac{4x}{x^2 - 1}$ or $\dfrac{4x}{1 - x^2}$

8. Yes

9. No

10. 5

11. $\dfrac{9}{2}$

12. $F = \dfrac{1}{2}$ or 0.5

13. $n = \dfrac{k + p}{p - 1}$

14. $x = 6$, $y = -7$

15. $x = 1$, $y = 4$

16. $x = 3$, $y = 2$ and $x = -3$, $y = 2$ and $x = 3$, $y = -2$ and $x = -3$, $y = -2$

17. $x = 3$, $y = 1$, $z = 2$

18. $x \geq 7$

19. $x > 5$

20. 1,508 trend-setters

Practice 115

a. $x = 1$, $y = 3$, $z = -4$

b. $-3 < x < 4$ (or it could also be written: $x > -3$ and $x < 4$)

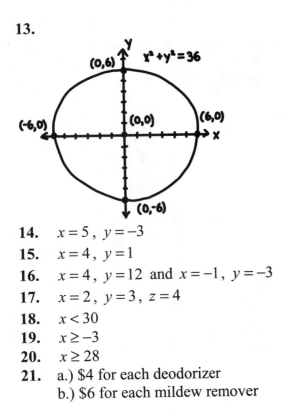

c. $x < -2$ or $x > 1$

d. $9 \leq x \leq 15$ (or it could also be written: $x \geq 9$ and $x \leq 15$)

e. \$3

Problem Set 115

1. True

2. True

3. True

4. $\dfrac{2}{3} p^6 q^8 r^7$

5. $\dfrac{3u^2 - 3uv}{uv + v^2}$

6. $\dfrac{1}{y+1}$

7. $\dfrac{5}{2}$

8. $5, 0$

9.

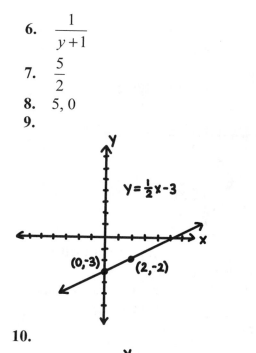

10.

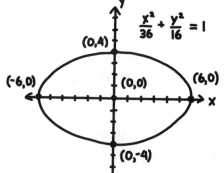

11. $y - 2 = -4(x - 2)$

12. $y - 1 = 1(x - 5)$ or $y + 3 = 1(x - 1)$

13. $x = 3, y = 6$

14. $x = 5, y = \dfrac{2}{3}$

15. $x = 1, y = 2, z = -3$

16. $-4 < x < 5$ (or it could also be written: $x > -4$ and $x < 5$)

17. $x < -1$ or $x > 3$

18. $x > \dfrac{2}{3}$

19. $y \leq -10$

20. $7 \leq x \leq 16$ (or it could also be written: $x \geq 7$ and $x \leq 16$)

21. $\$240$

Practice 116

a. $2x^2 - 5xy - 2y^2$

b. $x = 1, y = 5$ and $x = \dfrac{3}{2}, y = \dfrac{15}{2}$

c. $-6 < x < 6$ (or it could also be written: $x > -6$ and $x < 6$)

d. $x \leq -7$ or $x \geq 7$

e. More than 20 vacuums

Problem Set 116

1. -5

2. -6

3. $-7xyz(3y + x)$

4. $(y + 5a)(y + 4a)$

5. $-6a^4 b^5$

6. 1

7. $2x^2 - 3xy - 2y^2$

8. -2

9. $3, 1$

10. 4

11. $x = \dfrac{cd + b}{a}$

12. $x = 6, y = 1$

13. $x = 7, y = 2$

14. $x = 1, y = 7$ and $x = \dfrac{5}{2}, y = \dfrac{35}{2}$

15. $-2 < x < 4$ (or it could also be written: $x > -2$ and $x < 4$)

16. $x \leq -5$ or $x \geq 6$

17. $x \geq 9$

18. $x < -\dfrac{19}{5}$

19. $-10 < x < 10$ (or it could also be written: $x > -10$ and $x < 10$)

20. $x \le -8$ or $x \ge 8$

21. More than 100 wristwatches

Practice 117

a. All of the numbers less than or equal to -3 or greater than 11.

b. $x = -1$, $y = 5$, $z = -3$

c. $0 < x < 2$ (or it could also be written: $x > 0$ and $x < 2$)

d. $x \le -2$ or $x \ge 8$

e. a.) \$6 for each chicken biscuit bag
b.) \$5 for each parmesan biscuit bag

Problem Set 117

1. 3.88×10^{15}

2. 6.4×10^5

3. $\dfrac{64b^6}{a^8 c^4}$

4. $\dfrac{x-y}{x+y}$

5. $\dfrac{ab}{a^2 - 2ab + b^2}$

6. Yes

7. Yes

8. 3

9. $\dfrac{5}{8}$

10.

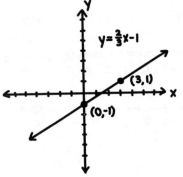

11.

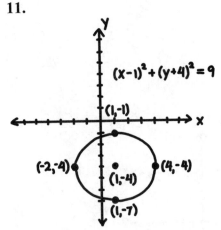

12. All of the numbers greater than -14 and less than 23.

13. All of the numbers less than or equal to -5 or greater than 9.

14. $x = 7$, $y = -14$

15. $x = 4$, $y = 15$

16. $x = -2$, $y = 6$, $z = -4$

17. $y \le -7$

18. $x \le -3$ or $x \ge -1$

19. $0 < x < 3$ (or it could also be written: $x > 0$ and $x < 3$)

20. $x \le -2$ or $x \ge 7$

21. a.) \$50 for each lifejacket
b.) \$40 for each paddle

Practice 118

a. $x = 3$, $y = 4$ and $x = 3$, $y = -4$ and $x = -3$, $y = 4$ and $x = -3$, $y = -4$

b. $y < -9$ or $y > 1$

c. When $x = 4$, $y \le -14$

d. $y \ge -\dfrac{7x}{3}$

e. 45 hours

Problem Set 118

1. True

2. False

3. $(a-b)(a-b)$ or $(a-b)^2$

4. $(7j + 8k)(7j - 8k)$

5. $56x^6y^5z^6$

6. $\dfrac{2x^2y}{z^2}$

7. $\dfrac{1}{3}$

8. $\sqrt{13}i - 7$, $-\sqrt{13}i - 7$

9. $a = 18$

10. $y = \dfrac{cdx - e}{a + b}$

11. $x = 2$, $y = 24$

12. $x = -3$, $y = 1$

13. $x = 3$, $y = 5$ and $x = 3$, $y = -5$ and $x = -3$, $y = 5$ and $x = -3$, $y = -5$

14. $-\dfrac{1}{2} \le x < \dfrac{7}{2}$ (or it could also be written: $x \ge -\dfrac{1}{2}$ and $x < \dfrac{7}{2}$)

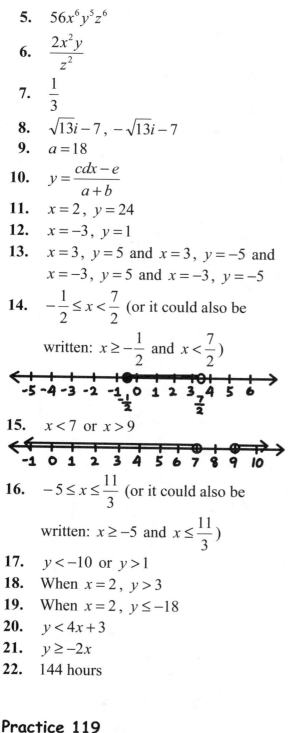

15. $x < 7$ or $x > 9$

16. $-5 \le x \le \dfrac{11}{3}$ (or it could also be written: $x \ge -5$ and $x \le \dfrac{11}{3}$)

17. $y < -10$ or $y > 1$

18. When $x = 2$, $y > 3$

19. When $x = 2$, $y \le -18$

20. $y < 4x + 3$

21. $y \ge -2x$

22. 144 hours

Practice 119

a. $x = -7$, $y = 1$, $z = -5$

b. $-\dfrac{7}{2} < x < 1$ (or it could also be written: $x > -\dfrac{7}{2}$ and $x < 1$)

c. $y > -5x$

d.

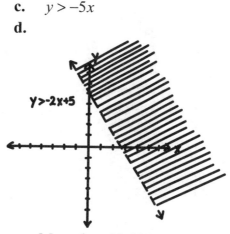

e. More than 20,000 onion peelers.

Problem Set 119

1. False
2. True
3. Perpendicular
4. Vertex $(2, 4)$; opens up
5. $5x^2 + 3y$
6. $\dfrac{x - y}{b}$
7. $-\dfrac{6}{7}$
8. $2, 0$
9. $y = 5x - 7$
10. $y - 1 = \dfrac{3}{4}(x - 1)$ or $y + 2 = \dfrac{3}{4}(x + 3)$
11. $x = -9$, $y = -4$
12. $x = -4$, $y = 1$, $z = -3$
13. $x \ge -8$
14. $x \le 3$ or $x \ge 5$
15. $-\dfrac{5}{2} < x < 1$ (or it could also be written: $x > -\dfrac{5}{2}$ and $x < 1$)
16. When $x = -3$, $y \ge 3$
17. When $x = -3$, $y < 9$
18. $y \ge \dfrac{-8x - 7}{2}$
19. $y > -4x$

20.

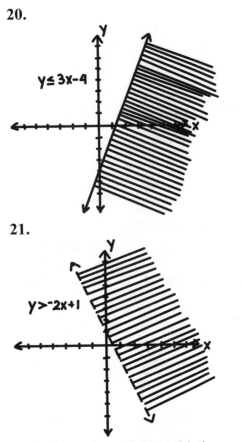

$y \leq 3x - 4$

21.

$y > {}^-2x + 1$

22. More than 30,000 whistles

Practice 120

a. $x = 5$, $y = 77$ and $x = -\dfrac{1}{3}$, $y = \dfrac{7}{3}$

b. $-3 < x < 9$ (or it could also be written: $x > -3$ and $x < 9$)

c. $x \leq -4$ or $x \geq 0$

d.

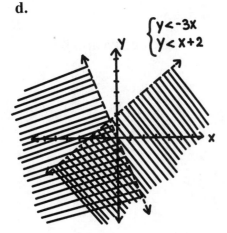

$\begin{cases} y < -3x \\ y < x + 2 \end{cases}$

e. a.) \$8 for each coffee mug
b.) \$14 for each t-shirt

Problem Set 120

1. True
2. True
3. $(rs^2 + tu^2)(rs^2 - tu^2)$
4. $(j + k)(j + k)$ or $(j + k)^2$
5. $2x^3 + 5x^2 y - xy^2 - y^3$
6. $a^3 c^3$
7. $\dfrac{3t + 3}{t^3 - 7t^2 - 25t + 175}$
8. $\dfrac{21}{10}$
9. 3
10. $z = -45$
11. $T = \dfrac{PV}{Nk_B}$
12. $x = -8$, $y = 3$
13. $x = 3$, $y = 28$ and $x = -\dfrac{1}{3}$, $y = \dfrac{4}{3}$
14. $x \geq -\dfrac{6}{17}$
15. $-5 < x < 20$ (or it could also be written: $x > -5$ and $x < 20$)
16. $x \leq -6$ or $x \geq 0$
17. $y \geq -\dfrac{2x + 3}{5}$
18. $y > x + 1$
19.

$\begin{cases} y \geq 2x - 1 \\ y \leq x \end{cases}$

20.

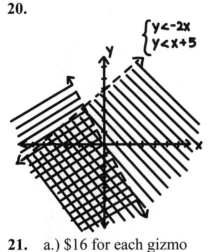

$$\begin{cases} y < -2x \\ y < x + 5 \end{cases}$$

21. a.) $16 for each gizmo
b.) $9 for each thingamajig

Practice 121

a. $\dfrac{1}{x^2 - 5xy + y^2}$

b. $x = 2$, $y = 6$, $z = -2$

c. $-2 < x < 8$ (or it could also be written: $x > -2$ and $x < 8$)

d. No solutions

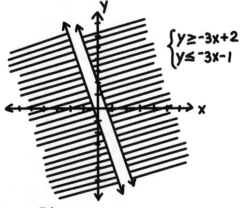

$$\begin{cases} y \geq -3x + 2 \\ y \leq {}^{-}3x - 1 \end{cases}$$

e. 7 hours

Problem Set 121

1. 4.89×10^8

2. 2.7×10^{-7}

3. $\sqrt{41}$

4. Center $(-2, 9)$; radius 12

5. $\dfrac{125x^9}{y^{12}z^3}$

6. $\dfrac{1}{x^2 - 3xy + y^2}$

7. No

8. Yes

9. 6

10. 4, -2

11. $x = 12$, $y = 3$

12. $x = 3$, $y = 7$, $z = -1$

13. $x > -\dfrac{7}{12}$

14. $x \geq 3$ or $x \leq -1$

15. $-2 < x < 7$ (or it could also be written: $x > -2$ and $x < 7$)

16. When $x = -\dfrac{1}{2}$, $y \geq -10$

17. When $x = -\dfrac{1}{2}$, $y < \dfrac{1}{2}$

18. $y \geq -\dfrac{5x}{3}$

19. $y > 8x + 9$

20.

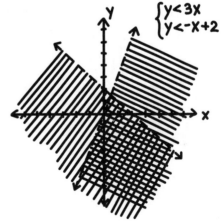

$$\begin{cases} y < 3x \\ y < -x + 2 \end{cases}$$

21. No solutions

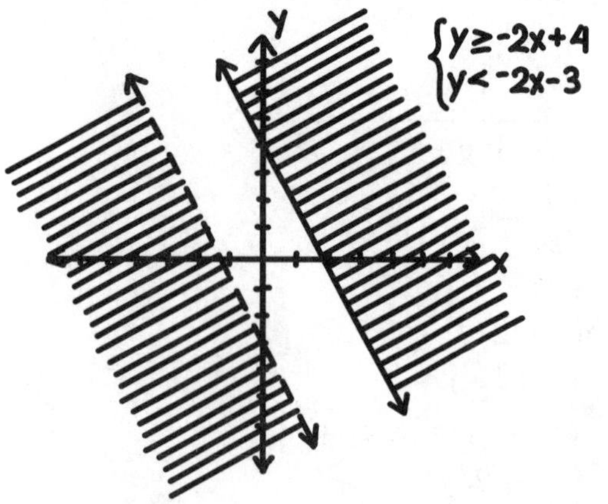

$$\begin{cases} y \geq -2x+4 \\ y < -2x-3 \end{cases}$$

22. 9 hours

CHAPTER 16

Practice 122

  a.   13

  b.   4

  c. $x = \dfrac{12}{5}$, $y = \dfrac{16}{5}$ and $x = -4$, $y = 0$

  d. $x \le -7$ or $x \ge 2$

  e.   More than 4,000 books

Problem Set 122

  1.   True

  2.   True

  3.   True

  4.   6

  5.   11

  6.   5

  7. $7x - 3$

  8. $\dfrac{m^2 + n^2}{m^2 - n^2}$

  9. $\dfrac{2}{x-3}$

10.   2

11. $3, -4$

12. $r = -4$

13. $v = \dfrac{cE}{B}$

14. $x = -3$, $y = -5$

15. $x = -4$, $y = 3$ and $x = 5$, $y = 0$

16. $x \le -\dfrac{13}{3}$

17. $-9 < x < 9$ (or it could also be written: $x > -9$ and $x < 9$)

18. $x \le -5$ or $x \ge 2$

19. $y < -3x + 4$

20. $y < 4x - 20$

21.

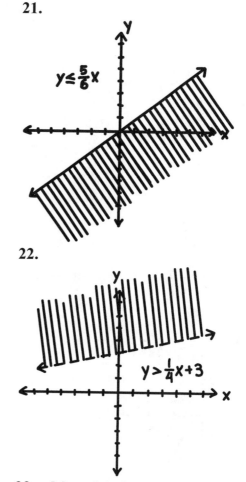

22.

23.   More than 20,000 books

Practice 123

  a. $x = 2$, $y = 9$, $z = 0$

  b. $-3 < x < -\dfrac{1}{3}$ (or it could also be written: $x > -3$ and $x < -\dfrac{1}{3}$)

  c. $19, -11$

  d. $8, -1$

  e.   a.) $28 for each bat

       b.) $4 for each baseball

Problem Set 123

1. True
2. True
3. 8
4. $\dfrac{1}{4}$
5. 9
6. $-\dfrac{2}{7}xy^2 + 5y$
7. $\dfrac{3}{2}$
8. -40
9. $\dfrac{26}{9}$
10. $y - 3 = \dfrac{5}{8}(x - 1)$
11. $y - 7 = 4(x + 9)$ or $y - 11 = 4(x + 8)$
12.

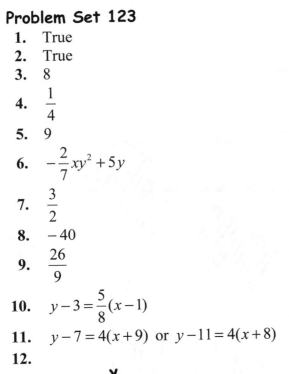

13.

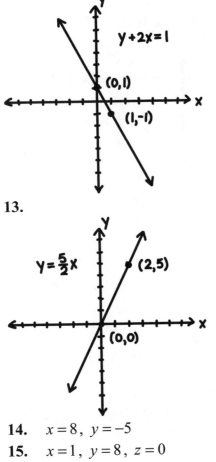

14. $x = 8$, $y = -5$
15. $x = 1$, $y = 8$, $z = 0$

16. $x < -6$
17. $x \le -6$ or $x \ge 3$
18. $-5 < x < -\dfrac{1}{3}$ (or it could also be

written: $x > -5$ and $x < -\dfrac{1}{3}$)

19. $7, -7$
20. $14, -8$
21. $4, -1$
22. a.) \$0.50 for each geranium
    b.) \$1 for each tulip bulb

Practice 124

a. $\dfrac{1}{x^4 y^4}$

b.

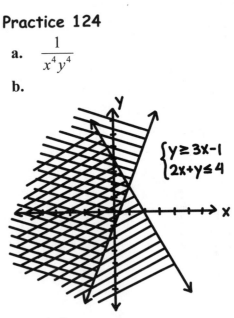

c. $4, 0$
d. No solutions
e. 300 seconds

Problem Set 124

1. False
2. False
3. 0
4. 1
5. $(5st + 4uv)(5st - 4uv)$
6. $(x + 2b)(x + b)$
7. $\dfrac{x^2 - 2x + 1}{x^2 + x}$

8. $\dfrac{1}{x^2 y^2}$

9. $\dfrac{44}{7}$

10. $3, -3$

11. $V = 268.16$

12. $m = \dfrac{p^2}{2E}$

13. $x = -2$, $y = -2$

14. $x = 3$, $y = 5$ and $x = -1$, $y = -3$

15. $y \geq -6$

16. $2 < x < 5$ (or it could also be written: $x > 2$ and $x < 5$)

17.

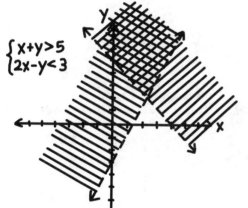

$\begin{cases} x+y>5 \\ 2x-y<3 \end{cases}$

18.

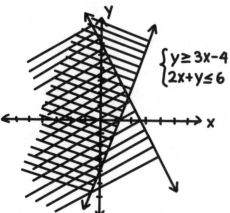

$\begin{cases} y \geq 3x-4 \\ 2x+y \leq 6 \end{cases}$

19. $17, -9$

20. $9, -5$

21. No solutions

22. $1,350$ seconds

Practice 125

a. $x = 1$, $y = 4$, $z = -2$

b. -4

c. $-1 \leq x \leq 11$ (or it could also be written: $x \geq -1$ and $x \leq 11$)

d. $x < -6$ or $x > \dfrac{7}{2}$

e. a.) \$60 for each pair of long-johns
   b.) \$80 for each pair of mittens

Problem Set 125

1. True

2. False

3. Parallel

4. Center $(0,0)$; vertices $(0,6)$, $(0,-6)$; opens up and down

5. $\dfrac{x}{3}$

6. $42a^6 b^5 c^5$

7. 14

8. $\sqrt{17}i$, $-\sqrt{17}i$

9. Yes

10. Yes

11. $x = 3$, $y = -2$

12. $x = 2$, $y = 3$, $z = -1$

13. $y \leq -10$ or $y \geq 20$

14. $-5 < x < 5$ (or it could also be written: $x > -5$ and $x < 5$)

15. $y > 8 - 2x$

16. $y \leq \dfrac{6x - 1}{5}$

17. $4, -4$

18. $13, 7$

19. -3

20. $-1 \leq x \leq 9$ (or it could also be written: $x \geq -1$ and $x \leq 9$)

21. $x < -4$ or $x > \dfrac{14}{5}$

22. a.) \$12 for each pack of diapers
    b.) \$3 for each jar of honey

ADDITIONAL TOPICS

Practice 126
a. $(s-t)(2c+3d)$

b. $2 < x < 8$ (or it could also be written: $x > 2$ and $x < 8$)

c. $-5 < x \leq \dfrac{2}{3}$ (or it could also be written: $x > -5$ and $x \leq \dfrac{2}{3}$)

d. $x \leq -3$ or $x \geq 2$

e. $\$350,000$

Problem Set 126
1. True
2. True
3. 9
4. 23
5. $(2n+7m)(2n-7m)$
6. $(x-y)(2a+3b)$
7. $-29xyz$
8. $\dfrac{x+y}{x-y}$
9. 1
10. $y = -21$
11. $h = \dfrac{j-1}{g+1}$
12. No solutions
13. $x = 6$, $y = 9$ and $x = 6$, $y = -9$ and $x = -6$, $y = 9$ and $x = -6$, $y = -9$
14. $-2 < x < 5$ (or it could also be written: $x > -2$ and $x < 5$)
15. $x < -4$ or $x > 1$
16. $-4 < x \leq \dfrac{5}{2}$ (or it could also be written: $x > -4$ and $x \leq \dfrac{5}{2}$)

17.

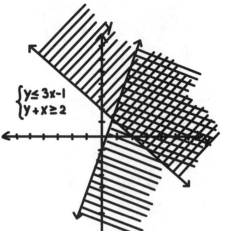

$\begin{cases} y \leq 3x-1 \\ y+x \geq 2 \end{cases}$

18.

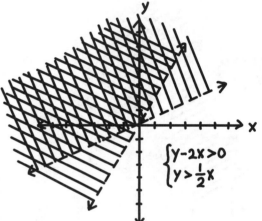

$\begin{cases} y-2x > 0 \\ y > \frac{1}{2}x \end{cases}$

19. $-5 < x < 9$ (or it could also be written: $x > -5$ and $x < 9$)
20. $x \leq -11$ or $x \geq 2$
21. $\$50$

Practice 127
a. $\dfrac{34}{53} + -\dfrac{13}{53}i$

b. $\dfrac{11}{37} + -\dfrac{45}{37}i$

c. $x \leq -9$ or $x \geq 3$

d. $x \leq -\dfrac{9}{2}$ or $x \geq 6$

e. More than 16,000 books

Problem Set 127

1. True
2. True
3. $-8 + 2i$
4. $\dfrac{16}{29} + \dfrac{11}{29}i$
5. $\dfrac{7}{26} + -\dfrac{17}{26}i$
6. $\dfrac{a^3}{b^3}$
7. $-\dfrac{x^2}{x^2 - y^2}$ or $\dfrac{x^2}{y^2 - x^2}$
8. $\dfrac{2}{7}$
9. $6, -8$
10. $y = \dfrac{1}{3}x + (-2)$
11. $y - 1 = 2(x - 1)$ or $y - 5 = 2(x - 3)$
12. $x = 10$, $y = 1$
13. $x = 4$, $y = 3$, $z = 2$
14. $x < -\dfrac{17}{4}$
15. $x \le -8$ or $x \ge 3$
16. $y < -8$ or $y > 7$
17. $6, -6$
18. $2, -\dfrac{3}{2}$
19. $2 < x < 8$ (or it could also be written: $x > 2$ and $x < 8$)
20. $x \le -\dfrac{21}{5}$ or $x \ge 5$
21. More than 28,000 books

Practice 128

a. No
b. $-4 \le x < 6$ (or it could also be written: $x \ge -4$ and $x < 6$)
c. No solutions
d. $x \le -26$ or $x \ge 10$

e. a.) $40 for each wiggler
   b.) $70 for each husky musky

Problem Set 128

1. True
2. True
3. $11 + 17i$
4. $-\dfrac{7}{5} + -\dfrac{19}{5}i$
5. Yes
6. No
7. $-35x^5y^9$
8. $\dfrac{1}{x - 2a}$
9. -33
10. $\dfrac{5}{3}$
11. $w = 2$
12. $v = \dfrac{cF}{Be}$
13. $x = 3$, $y = 2$
14. $x = -2$, $y = 2$
15. $y > 8$
16. $-6 \le x < 2$ (or it could also be written: $x \ge -6$ and $x < 2$)
17. $4, -5$
18. No solutions
19. $-\dfrac{9}{5} < x < 3$ (or it could also be written: $x > -\dfrac{9}{5}$ and $x < 3$)
20. $x \le -20$ or $x \ge 8$
21. a.) $20 for each small pillow
    b.) $45 for each large pillow

Practice 129

a. No
b. Yes
c. Domain = all real numbers
   Range = all real numbers greater than or equal to 3

d. $-3 \le x \le 0$ (or it could also be written: $x \ge -3$ and $x \le 0$)

e. 135 people

Problem Set 129

1. False
2. True
3. True
4. $-14+(-22i)$
5. $-\dfrac{11}{41}+\dfrac{58}{41}i$
6. $5\sqrt{2}$
7. Vertex $(0,0)$; opens down
8. Yes
9. No
10. Yes
11. Domain = all real numbers
    Range = all real numbers
12. Domain = all real numbers
    Range = all real numbers greater than or equal to 8
13. $x^3 + x^2 y - xy^2 - y^3$
14. $\dfrac{4a^2}{ab - b^2}$
15. Yes
16. No
17. $x \ge -2$
18. $x < -\dfrac{1}{3}$ or $x > 3$
19. $-2 \le x \le 0$ (or it could also be written: $x \ge -2$ and $x \le 0$)
20. $-17 \le x \le -5$ (or it could also be written: $x \ge -17$ and $x \le -5$)
21. $x < -18$ or $x > -6$
22. 322 people

Practice 130

a. $f(-3) = 27$
b. Domain = all real numbers except 0
   Range = all real numbers except 0
c. $y \le -1$ or $y \ge 2$

d. $-2 \le x \le \dfrac{22}{3}$ (or it could also be written: $x \ge -2$ and $x \le \dfrac{22}{3}$)

e. 150 seconds

Problem Set 130

1. True
2. True
3. $f(3) = 3$
4. $f(-2) = 8$
5. Domain = all real numbers
   Range = all real numbers less than or equal to 0
6. Domain = all real numbers except 0
   Range = all real numbers except 0
7. $xy(x - y^2)$
8. $(a-b)^2$ or $(a-b)(a-b)$
9. $3r^4 s^5$
10. $\dfrac{9}{49}x^4 y^4 t^2$
11. 5
12. $\sqrt{13}i$, $-\sqrt{13}i$
13. $x = 7$, $y = 6$
14. $x = 4$, $y = 5$, $z = -1$
15. $x > 3$
16. $y \le 1$ or $y \ge 6$
17.

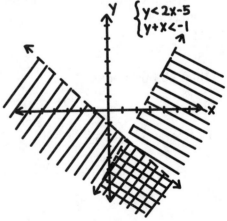

80

18.

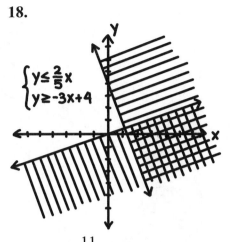

$$\begin{cases} y \le \frac{2}{5}x \\ y \ge -3x+4 \end{cases}$$

19. $x < -\dfrac{11}{5}$ or $x > 3$

20. $-3 \le x \le 10$ (or it could also be written: $x \ge -3$ and $x \le 10$)

21. 160 seconds

$$\left(\sqrt{5x-1}\right)^2 = \left(\sqrt{x}\right)^2 \quad \text{square first}$$

normally

$$5 \quad = x^2$$

CHAPTER TESTS

paraboloid

$$7^{\frac{1}{2}} \cdot 7^{\frac{1}{3}} = 7^{\frac{1}{2}+\frac{1}{3}} = 7^{\frac{5}{6}}$$

z-axis

$$(3+2i)+(4$$

x-axis

$$3+2i+$$

y-axis

3-variable
equation
= 3-D surface

total momen

$$3\text{-variable} \begin{cases} 5x + 3y - 2z = 0 \\ x - 7y + z = 2 \\ 3x + y - 4z = 1 \end{cases}$$

Chapter 1 Test

Tell whether each sentence below is True or False.

1. Algebra is a language for problem solving that has its own "grammar."

2. Addition and multiplication are inverse operations, which means that they will undo each other.

3. Equations with more than one operation are solved by undoing those operations in reverse order.

Complete each sentence below with the best of the choices given.

4. According to the order of operations rules, all _____ are done before _____ .

    A. additions and subtractions; multiplications and divisions
    B. multiplications and divisions; additions and subtractions
    C. divisions and subtractions; multiplications and additions
    D. multiplications and additions; divisions and subtractions
    E. multiplications and subtractions; divisions and additions

5. To add two negative numbers, you add the magnitude of the numbers (ignoring their signs) and make the answer _____ .

    A. positive
    B. zero
    C. negative
    D. equal to the larger number
    E. none of the above

Calculate the value of each expression below.

6. $8 \cdot 2 + 9$

7. $5(8 - 2)$

8. $(11)(-4)$

9. $-21 - 16$

10. $\dfrac{-56}{-8}$

Translate each phrase below into a mathematical expression. (Don't do the calculation.)

11. the sum of 3 and 6, all multiplied by -9

12. the quotient of -15 and 5 decreased by 8

Write an equation to represent each problem below. (Don't solve the equation.)

13. If the sum of some number and 12 is divided by 3, the result is equal to 20.

14. The product of some number and 4 is decreased by 7 and the result is 18.

State whether each pair of fractions below have the same value.

15. $\dfrac{2}{-5}$ and $-\dfrac{2}{5}$

16. $\dfrac{-3}{-11}$ and $-\dfrac{3}{11}$

Solve each equation below by undoing.

17. $x-(-7)=29$

18. $5x+11=46$

19. $\dfrac{x-4}{2}=\dfrac{5}{2}$

20. $\dfrac{-x}{6}+1=18$

21. $3(x-12)=51$

22. $\dfrac{1}{2}x-1=-\dfrac{1}{3}$

23. $-3.2-x=-19.4$

24. $\dfrac{1}{2}\left(x+\dfrac{2}{3}\right)=\dfrac{5}{4}$

Translate the word problem below into an equation; then solve.

25. Because of inflation, Frank's Frankfurters Incorporated increased the price of their award-winning hot dogs by $2. But when sales nose-dived, the company was forced to cut the new price in half to sell all the extra hot dogs they had in stock. If the final price of the hotdogs was $2.50, what was the original price?

Chapter 2 Test

Tell whether each sentence below is True or False.

1. Simplify means to rewrite an expression in a simpler form without changing its value.

2. When distributing to free an x from more than one set of parentheses, you distribute over the innermost set first.

Complete each sentence below with the best of the choices given.

3. The _____ states that the order in which two numbers are multiplied won't affect the answer.

    A. commutative property of addition
    B. commutative property of multiplication
    C. associative property of addition
    D. associative property of multiplication
    E. distributive property

4. In letters, the associative property of addition is shown by the statement _____.

    A. $a+b=b+a$
    B. $ab=ba$
    C. $(a+b)+c=a+(b+c)$
    D. $a(b+c)=ab+ac$
    E. none of the above

Calculate the value of each expression below.

5. $\dfrac{5+(-9)}{-2}$

6. $-(2+7)-3(-5)$

7. $3[1+5(4-2)]$

Tell whether each pair of expressions below is equivalent.

8. $\dfrac{x-7}{3}$ and $\dfrac{1}{3}x-\dfrac{7}{3}$

9. $3x+4[2(x+1)+5]$ and $11x+28$

86

Simplify each expression below.

10. $5.1x + (-2.7x)$

11. $-6 + 8x + 9$

12. $y - \dfrac{2y}{5}$

13. $\dfrac{4}{5}(x + 10)$

14. $3(x - 6) - 7(x + 1)$

15. $5[2(x - 4)]$

Solve each equation below. Indicate any false equations or identities.

16. $2.8 + 2x + 0.9 = 17.7$

17. $\dfrac{1}{4}x + \dfrac{1}{2}x = 12$

18. $8x + 5 = 3x - 7$

19. $9x + 4(x - 3) = 14$

20. $\dfrac{y}{2} + y = -1$

21. $7(x - 3) = -21 + 7x$

22. $2x + \dfrac{x - 6}{2} = 0$

23. $5x \cdot 2 = 10x + 3$

24. $4x + 2[3(x - 1) + 2] = 8$

Translate the word problem below into an equation; then solve.

25. Mr. Cash invested \$80,000 in various stocks and bonds. He earned a 7% dividend on his stocks and 5% interest on his bonds, for a one year profit (from both stocks and bonds) of \$4,900. How much did Mr. Cash invest in bonds?

Chapter 3 Test

Tell whether each sentence below is True or False.

1. When a fraction has an x in its denominator, that x can't have a value that will make the denominator equal zero.

2. When multiplying fractions with x's, it's easier to factor and cancel after multiplying.

3. To clear more than one fraction from an equation, you multiply both sides by the lowest common denominator of the fractions.

Calculate the value of each expression below.

4. $8(-2)-(-5)(6)$

5. $-5[10-3(7+4)]$

6. $\dfrac{9-21}{-7+3}$

Simplify each expression below.

7. $\dfrac{8x+4}{6x+3}$

8. $\dfrac{5x}{4}\cdot\dfrac{12}{25x}$

9. $\dfrac{x-4}{18x}\div\dfrac{2x-8}{9}$

10. $\dfrac{x+5}{2x}-\dfrac{3x+2}{x}$

11. $3[-4(x+2)+1]$

12. $\dfrac{5x}{2x+6}+\dfrac{x-3}{x+3}$

Tell whether each pair of expressions below is equivalent.

13. $\dfrac{3x+19}{3x}$ and 19

14. $-\dfrac{y}{2}-3y$ and $-5y$

Solve each equation below. Indicate any false equations or identities.

15. $\dfrac{5}{9x}=1$

16. $\dfrac{1}{x-7}=-8$

17. $24-3x=-6x+22$

18. $3[4(x-2)+x]=21$

19. $\dfrac{2x+10}{2}=-43$

20. $\dfrac{5}{3x+6}=\dfrac{2}{9x}$

21. $8x+11-x=7x$

22. $\dfrac{2x}{3}+\dfrac{x}{2}=\dfrac{5}{6}$

23. $\dfrac{4}{5x+15}-\dfrac{1}{x+3}=\dfrac{3}{5}$

Translate the word problem below into an equation; then solve.

24. Margaret went to the convenience store and purchased 4 cans of cola for $2.76. How many cans could she have purchased (at the same price) for $13.11?

Chapter 4 Test

Tell whether each sentence below is True or False.

1. A power is a shortcut for writing a repeated multiplication.

2. Terms with x's raised to the same power are called like terms.

3. The shortcut for multiplying powers is to add their exponents.

Calculate the value of each expression below.

4. $5 \cdot 3^2 - 7$

5. $\dfrac{4^2 - 2^3}{-2}$

6. $-3(2+5)^2$

Rewrite each number below in scientific notation.

7. 5,400,000,000

8. 0.000000027

Calculate the value of each expression below. Leave your answers in scientific notation.

9. $(3.2 \times 10^7)(5.6 \times 10^4)$

10. $\dfrac{(1.2 \times 10^9)(4.4 \times 10^8)}{3.0 \times 10^{21}}$

Tell whether each of the following pairs of expressions is equivalent.

11. $3x^{-6}$ and $\dfrac{3}{x^6}$

12. $-2x^5 + 3x^4 + 9x^5 - 8x^4$ and $7x^5 - 5x^4$

Simplify each expression below.

13. $(6x^8)(9x^7)$

14. $\dfrac{y^2 + 8y + 15}{y^2 + 7y + 10}$

15. $(x+5)(x^2 + 3x + 2)$

16. $\dfrac{x^2 - 6x + 5}{3x^2} \div \dfrac{2x - 10}{9x}$

17. $\dfrac{5}{x+3} + \dfrac{2x}{x^2 + 6x + 9}$

18. $\dfrac{z^3 + 1}{2z^2 + 4z} - \dfrac{3z^2}{z+2}$

Solve each equation below.

19. $-4.2x + 3 = -9 + 1.8x$

20. $\dfrac{3x}{2} = \dfrac{x}{2} + 4$

21. $-3(x + 7) = 2(x - 1)$

22. $\dfrac{2}{5x} + \dfrac{x+1}{x} = 2$

23. $3[x + 2(x + 4)] = 60$

24. $\dfrac{4x}{3x - 12} = \dfrac{1}{x - 4}$

Translate the word problem below into an equation; then solve.

25. Mr. Pyle, the gasoline station attendant, mixed $1.95 per gallon unleaded gas with 65 gallons of $2.15 per gallon premium gas to create a $2.00 gas blend called *Budget Premium*. How many gallons of the unleaded gas did Mr. Pyle use?

Chapter 5 Test

Tell whether each sentence below is True or False.

1. The inverse of raising a number to a power is taking a root.

2. To multiply irrationals, multiply the numbers under the radical signs and take the root of the result.

Rewrite each number below in regular decimal form.

3. 1.48×10^7 **4.** 7.6×10^{-4}

Tell whether each number below is rational or irrational.

5. $\sqrt[3]{4}$ **6.** $\sqrt{81}$

Give a decimal estimate to two places (hundredths) for each irrational number below.

7. $\sqrt{13}$ **8.** $\sqrt{17}$

Change each root below into a power.

9. $\sqrt{5}$ **10.** $\sqrt[5]{3^2}$

Answer each question below.

11. Multiply $\sqrt{11} \cdot \sqrt{2}$. **12.** Combine $7\sqrt{3} + \sqrt{12}$. **13.** Divide $\dfrac{\sqrt[3]{20}}{\sqrt[3]{5}}$.

14. Multiply $\sqrt[3]{7} \cdot \sqrt{7}$ using fractional exponents.

15. Divide $\dfrac{\sqrt{2}}{\sqrt[5]{2}}$ using fractional exponents.

16. Simplify $\dfrac{\sqrt{5}}{\sqrt{7}}$ by rationalizing the denominator.

Factor each expression below.

17. $21y^3 + 14y^2$

18. $x^2 - 9x + 20$

Simplify each expression below.

19. $(3^2 x^4)^{-3}$

20. $\dfrac{x^2 - 2x - 8}{3x^2 + 9x} \cdot \dfrac{3x - 18}{x + 2}$

21. $\dfrac{3y}{y^2 + 3y - 10} - \dfrac{5}{2y + 10}$

Solve each equation below.

22. $7y - (9 + 4y) = -3$

23. $\dfrac{2z - 1}{3} - \dfrac{3z + 1}{5} = 1$

24. $\dfrac{7}{3x + 1} = \dfrac{2}{x + 2}$

Translate the word problem below into an equation; then solve.

25. Truck #1 and truck #2 left from the same location at the same time, driving in opposite directions. If truck #1 traveled at 70 mph and truck #2 at 65 mph, how many hours was it before they were 1,755 miles apart?

Chapter 6 Test

Tell whether each sentence below is True or False.

1. Second-degree equations can never have two solutions.

2. The quadratic formula can be used to solve second-degree equations that are too hard to factor.

Calculate the value of each expression below. Leave your answer in scientific notation.

3. $(4.2 \times 10^9)(3.2 \times 10^{-13})$

4. $\dfrac{2.1 \times 10^{10}}{7 \times 10^{17}}$

Answer each question below.

5. Multiply $(\sqrt{5} + 2)(\sqrt{5} - 9)$.

6. Simplify $\dfrac{\sqrt{2}}{\sqrt{3} - \sqrt{7}}$ by rationalizing the denominator.

7. Divide $\dfrac{11^{\frac{4}{5}}}{11^{\frac{1}{5}}}$.

Factor each expression below.

8. $x^2 - 5x - 36$

9. $2x^2 + 7x + 5$

Simplify each expression below.

10. $\dfrac{(3x^{-4})^3}{5x^2}$

11. $\dfrac{\dfrac{y+2}{4y^2}}{\dfrac{3y+6}{2y^3}}$

12. $\dfrac{x}{x-4} + \dfrac{2}{x^2 - 4x}$

Tell whether each of the following pairs of expressions is equivalent.

13. $\frac{1}{3}x^2 + \frac{x^2}{4}$ and $\frac{7}{12}x^2$

14. $(x+4)(x+5)(x+1)$ and $3x+10$

Solve each equation below. Be sure to give *every* solution.

15. $\frac{3x-5}{7} = 0$ **16.** $2x^2 - 3 = 19$ **17.** $(x+5)^2 - 18 = 63$

Solve each equation below by factoring. Be sure to give *every* solution.

18. $2x^2 + 8x = 0$ **19.** $x^2 - 10x = -21$ **20.** $2x^2 - 3x = 5$

Solve the equation below by completing the square. Be sure to give *every* solution.

21. $x^2 + 4x - 1 = 0$

Solve each equation below using the quadratic formula: $x = \dfrac{-b \pm \sqrt{b^2 - 4ac}}{2a}$. Be sure to give *every* solution.

22. $2x^2 + 5x - 1 = 0$ **23.** $3x^2 + 7x = 1$

Translate the word problem below into an equation; then solve.

24. One positive integer is 5 times another positive integer and their product is 320. What are the positive integers?

Chapter 7 Test

Tell whether each sentence below is True or False.

1. Equations with an x under a radical sign are called radical equations.

2. It is always necessary to check the solutions to a radical equation.

Find the values for a, b, and c for each quadratic equation below.

3. $4x^2 + 2x - 1 = 0$

4. $3x^2 - 5x = 11$

Answer each question below.

5. Combine $3\sqrt{12} + 2\sqrt{3}$.

6. Divide $\dfrac{\sqrt{35}}{\sqrt{5}}$.

7. Multiply $\sqrt[4]{5} \cdot \sqrt[3]{5}$ using fractional exponents.

Factor each expression below.

8. $18x^3 + 9x^2$

9. $x^2 - 8x - 20$

10. $2x^2 - 5x + 3$

Simplify each expression below.

11. $(5z^2)(4z^{-6})$

12. $\dfrac{x-2}{3x^3} \cdot \dfrac{9x^2}{x^2 - 4x + 4}$

13. $\dfrac{5}{x-3} - \dfrac{2x+4}{x^2 - 4x + 3}$

Tell whether each pair of expressions below is equivalent.

14. $\dfrac{6x - 15x^3}{-10x^3 + 4x}$ and $\dfrac{3}{2}$

15. $8x^2 + 18x - 5$ and $(4x - 1)(2x + 5)$

Solve each equation below. Be sure to give *every* solution.

16. $\dfrac{1}{2x} - \dfrac{3}{5x} = 1$ **17.** $2\sqrt{x} - 4 = 10$ **18.** $\sqrt{5x-1} = 2$

19. $\sqrt{x-2} = x - 4$ **20.** $\dfrac{1}{\sqrt{x+3}} = \sqrt{-2x}$ **21.** $\sqrt{x+9} - \sqrt{2x-7} = 0$

Solve each equation below by factoring or by using the quadratic formula: $x = \dfrac{-b \pm \sqrt{b^2 - 4ac}}{2a}$.
Be sure to give *every* solution.

22. $y^2 + 2y = 35$ **23.** $2x^2 + 5x - 5 = 0$

Translate the word problem below into an equation; then solve.

24. Benny the carhop has 2 times as many dimes as quarters. If Benny has $41.85 worth of dimes and quarters combined, how many quarters does he have?

Chapter 8 Test

Tell whether each sentence below is True or False.

1. Imaginary numbers are used to allow numbers to represent not two, but four directions.

2. Complex numbers make it possible to represent more than four directions.

Use the discriminate to tell whether the solutions of each equation below are real or complex.

3. $x^2 + 5x + 2 = 0$

4. $4x^2 - 3x + 9 = 0$

Write each imaginary number below using i. Make sure to fully simplify your answers.

5. $\sqrt{-81}$

6. $\sqrt{-20}$

Write a complex number to represent each quantity below.

7. The quantity 4 units to the north.

8. The quantity $\sqrt{11}$ units to the south.

Calculate the value of each imaginary or complex number expression below. Make sure to fully simplify your answers.

9. $(1 + 4i) + (9 + 8i)$

10. $\sqrt{2}i \cdot \sqrt{6}i$

11. $(7 + 5i) - (-2 + -3i)$

12. $-23i^6$

13. $(5 + 2i)(1 + 3i)$

14. $\dfrac{11i}{\sqrt{2}i}$

15. $(2i)^5$

Simplify each expression below.

16. $(5y^7)^{-3}$

17. $\dfrac{y^2 - 10y + 25}{3y - 15}$

18. $\dfrac{x + 2}{2x - 2} + \dfrac{4x - 3}{10x - 10}$

Solve each equation below. Be sure to give *every* solution.

19. $5x - 10x^2 = 0$

20. $\dfrac{\sqrt{2x+7}}{4} = 3$

21. $x^2 = -29$

22. $\sqrt{x^2 + 11} = 6$

23. $(x+6)^2 = -9$

Solve the equation below by using the quadratic formula: $x = \dfrac{-b \pm \sqrt{b^2 - 4ac}}{2a}$. Be sure to give *every* solution.

24. $x^2 + 3x + 8 = 0$

Translate the word problem below into an equation; then solve.

25. The second angle of the triangle is twice the first, while the third angle of the triangle is 1.5 times the second. What is the measure of the first angle? (Remember, the sum of the angles in any triangle is 180 degrees.)

Chapter 9 Test

Tell whether each sentence below is True or False.

1. A polynomial is an expression with x's that have only whole number exponents.

2. Polynomial division is an algebra version of long division.

Give a decimal estimate to two places (hundredths) for each irrational number below.

3. $3 + \sqrt{14}$

4. $\dfrac{-2 - \sqrt{51}}{3}$

Use the discriminate to tell whether the solutions of each equation below are real or complex.

5. $3x^2 - 2x + 1 = 0$

6. $x^2 - 7x + 3 = 0$

7. $-2x^2 + 5x - 4 = 0$

Calculate the value of each imaginary or complex number expression below. Make sure to fully simplify your answers.

8. $(-4 + 7i) + (-2 + 5i)$

9. $(-3i^4)^3$

10. $(-3 + i)(8 + 2i)$

Factor each expression below. Make sure to factor each expression completely.

11. $x^2 - 4x + 3$

12. $2x^2 - 13x - 7$

13. $x^3 + 7x^2 + 12x$

Simplify each expression below.

14. $-11x^5 + (7x^5)$

15. $\dfrac{6y}{10y^3} \div \dfrac{18y^2}{5y^3}$

16. $2x^2(x^3 - 8x)$

17. $\dfrac{5 - 2x}{4x + 12x^2} - \dfrac{5 - 6x}{4x + 12x^2}$

18. $\dfrac{2x^3 + 11x^2 + 13x + 4}{x + 4}$

Solve each equation below. Be sure to give *every* solution.

19. $\dfrac{9-3x}{2} = 5x$

20. $x^3 + 4x^2 + 3x = 0$

21. $\sqrt{8x-9} = \sqrt{15+7x}$

22. $x^4 - 9x^2 + 18 = 0$

23. $x^2 = -19$

24. $x^3 - 2x^2 - x + 2 = 0$

Translate the word problem below into an equation; then solve.

25. Hank and Aaron are 875 miles apart and headed straight toward each other. If Hank is traveling at 65 mph and Aaron is traveling at 60 mph, how many hours will it be before the two meet?

Chapter 10 Test

Tell whether each sentence below is True or False.

1. A relationship between changing quantities can be shown with a table, an equation, or a picture (graph).

2. The graph of a linear equation (a first-degree equation with two variables) is a circle.

Calculate the value of each expression below.

3. $20 - [-2(5-1)^2 + 9]$

4. $\dfrac{4(1+2)^2}{-6+3}$

Factor each expression below.

5. $6x^2 - 10x$

6. $5x^2 - 11x + 2$

Simplify each expression below.

7. $(\dfrac{3}{4}z)(-8z^3)^2$

8. $\dfrac{x^2 + 2x - 15}{4x} \cdot \dfrac{2x^4}{x^3 + 5x^2}$

9. $\dfrac{x^3 + 4x^2 - 2x - 5}{x + 1}$

Solve each equation below.

10. $\dfrac{x}{2} - 5 = 3x + 4$

11. $x^3 - 7x^2 = -12x$

12. $\sqrt{x+5} - 5 = x$

Complete the table for the two-variable equation below.

13. $y = -2x + 6$

x	-2	-1	0	1	2	3
y	10	8	6	4		

Graph the two-variable equation below.

14. $y = 3x - 2$

Answer each question below.

15. In the equation $y = 5x - 8$, find the value of y when $x = -4$.

16. In the equation $y = -9x$, find the value of y when $x = \dfrac{1}{3}$.

Solve each two-variable equation below for y in terms of x, then simplify.

17. $2y = 6x + 8$ **18.** $3x - y = 5$

Find the rate of change for each two-variable equation below.

19. $y = -\dfrac{3}{2}x + 1$ **20.** $y - 4x = -7$ **21.** $y - x = 0$

Find the slope of the line below.

22.

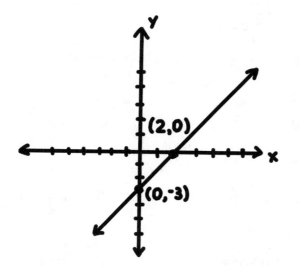

Write the equation for each line described below.

23. The line crossing the point $(2, 5)$ and with slope $= 4$.

24. The line crossing the point $(0, 3)$ and with slope $= -\dfrac{1}{5}$.

Translate the word problem below into an equation; then solve.

25. It takes Ron 4 seconds to stack a shingle and Ben 3 seconds to do the same. How many seconds will it take the two of them together to stack on 91 shingles?

Chapter 11 Test

Tell whether each sentence below is True or False.

1. An equation for an ellipse with its center at the origin looks like $\dfrac{x^2}{a^2} + \dfrac{y^2}{b^2} = 1$, with a and b representing the horizontal and vertical distances from the center to the edges.

2. An equation for a hyperbola with its center at the origin and opening left and right looks like $\dfrac{x^2}{a^2} - \dfrac{y^2}{b^2} = 1$, with the points $(a, 0)$ and $(-a, 0)$ representing the vertices.

Answer each question below.

3. Tell whether the lines for $y - \dfrac{3}{5}x = 0$ and $y = -\dfrac{5}{3}x + 2$ are parallel or perpendicular.

4. Tell whether the line for $x = 7$ is horizontal or vertical.

5. Which of the following equations represents a parabola that opens downward and has a vertex at the origin?

    A. $y = -\dfrac{1}{8}x^2$ B. $y = x^2 - 2x + 1$ C. $y = 5x^2$

    D. $y = -3x^2 + 11x$ E. $y = -2x^2 + 4x + 3$

6. Which of the following equations represents a parabola that opens upward and has a vertex that is *not* at the origin?

    A. $y = -\dfrac{1}{8}x^2$ B. $y = x^2 - 2x + 1$ C. $y = 5x^2$

    D. $y = -3x^2 + 11x$ E. $y = -2x^2 + 4x + 3$

7. Tell the vertex of the parabola for the equation $y - 1 = 2(x - 3)^2$, and tell whether the parabola opens up or down.

8. Tell the center and radius of the circle for the equation $(x + 4)^2 + (y - 7)^2 = 25$.

Simplify each expression below.

9. $6x^4 + (-10x^4) + 2x^4$

10. $(3y^{-5})^{-3}$

11. $\dfrac{x^2 - 3x - 10}{2x^2 + x - 6}$

Solve each equation below.

12. $\dfrac{1}{x-1} = \dfrac{2}{3} + \dfrac{2}{x-1}$

13. $\dfrac{3x}{2} - 3 = 2x$

14. $\sqrt{9x - 28} = \sqrt{5x}$

Graph each two-variable equation below.

15. $y = \dfrac{1}{2}x - 4$

16. $y = -2x^2$

17. $\dfrac{x^2}{2^2} + \dfrac{y^2}{4^2} = 1$

18. $\dfrac{x^2}{5^2} - \dfrac{y^2}{3^2} = 1$

Solve each two-variable equation below for y in terms of x, then simplify.

19. $4y + 3x = 0$

20. $2y + x = 12$

Find the slope and y-intercept of the graph of each linear equation below.

21. $y - \dfrac{1}{2}x = -5$

22. $x - 3y = 0$

Write the equation for each line described below.

23. The line crossing the point $(0, -9)$ and with slope $= 4$.

24. The line crossing the points $(2, -8)$ and $(-1, -2)$.

Translate the word problem below into an equation; then solve.

25. The ratio of diners to snackers at the food court was 4 to 7. If there were 148 diners, how many snackers were there?

Chapter 12 Test

Tell whether each sentence below is True or False.

1. Each solution to a three-variable equation has three numbers.

2. Three–variable equations can be graphed on a coordinate plane and their graphs are all either parabolas or circles.

Calculate the value of each imaginary or complex number expression below. Make sure to fully simplify your answers.

3. $(-2i)^4$

4. $(2+7i)(-9+i)$

Answer each question below.

5. Find the distance between the points $(-2, -5)$ and $(3, 2)$ on the coordinate plane.

6. Tell the vertex of the parabola for the equation $y = 2x^2 + 8x + 11$, and tell whether the parabola opens up or down.

7. Tell the center and vertices of the hyperbola for the equation $\dfrac{x^2}{4^2} - \dfrac{y^2}{2^2} = 1$, and tell whether the hyperbola opens left and right or up and down.

Simplify each expression below.

8. $(x-2)(x^2 + 4x - 3)$

9. $\dfrac{8z^7}{5z^5} \div \dfrac{14z^9}{15z^3}$

10. $\dfrac{x+2}{10x^2} + \dfrac{3}{20x}$

Solve each equation below.

11. $2[3(x+4)] - 15 = 4x$

12. $y^2 - 3y = 40$

13. $\sqrt{x} = x - 2$

Answer each question below.

14. In the equation $f = \dfrac{a^2 - b^2}{c}$, find the value of f when $a = -5$, $b = -2$, and $c = 7$.

15. Solve for u in the equation $Q = \frac{1}{4}st^2u$, then simplify.

16. Solve for x in the equation $ax - b = x$, then simplify.

Graph each two-variable equation below.

17. $y = 0x - 3$

18. $\frac{(x-2)^2}{5^2} + \frac{(y-2)^2}{3^2} = 1$

19. $(x+1)^2 + (y+3)^2 = 4^2$

Find the slope of the line below.

20.

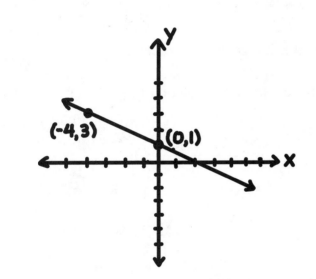

Write the equation for each line described below.

21. The line crossing the point $(0, 8)$ and with slope $= -\frac{1}{5}$.

22. The line crossing the point $(1, 4)$ and with slope $= 3$.

23. The line crossing the points $(3, 5)$ and $(2, 7)$.

Translate the word problem below into an equation; then solve.

24. Todd is 7 years old and Sean is 9 years old. Their father, Sam, is 44 years old. How long will it be before the sum of the children's ages is half of his?

Chapter 13 Test

Tell whether each sentence below is True or False.

1. For terms to be "like terms" and combinable, each of the variables (the x's, y's, and z's) must be raised to the same power.

2. Two of the most common standard forms are $(x+a)^2$, which equals $x^2 + 2ax + a^2$, and $(x-a)^2$, which equals $x^2 - 2ax + a^2$.

Answer each question below.

3. Find the distance between the points $(5\frac{1}{2}, 0)$ and $(2\frac{1}{2}, 4)$ on the coordinate plane.

4. Tell whether the line for $y = -9$ is horizontal or vertical.

5. Tell the center and radius of the circle for the equation $(x+3)^2 + (y-5)^2 = 64$.

Factor each expression below.

6. $7a^3bc^2 + 14a^2b^3c$

7. $x^2 - 2xy + y^2$

8. $4s^2 - 25t^2$

9. $ah + ak + bh + bk$

Simplify each expression below.

10. $11xy^2z^3 + (-7xy^2z^3)$

11. $(-3f^3g^4h^2)^2$

12. $2s^3t^2(5st - s^3t)$

13. $\dfrac{x^2 - 2xy + y^2}{bx + cb} \cdot \dfrac{x^2 + cx}{x^2 - y^2}$

14. $\dfrac{\dfrac{a}{b^2} \cdot \dfrac{b}{2a^2}}{\dfrac{3ab}{b^3} \cdot \dfrac{b^2}{2a^2}}$

15. $\dfrac{2x^3 + x^2y - 2xy^2 - y^3}{x - y}$

Solve each equation below.

16. $-5(x+2) + 3x = 12$

17. $(x+6)^2 = -13$

18. $x^2 - 8x + 7 = 0$

Answer each question below.

19. In the equation $y = ax^2 + bx + c$, find the value of y when $a = 3$, $b = -4$, $c = 1$, and $x = -2$.

20. Solve for q in the equation $p = \dfrac{x+q}{y+q}$, then simplify.

Graph each two-variable equation below.

21. $x^2 + y^2 = 9$ **22.** $\dfrac{(x-2)^2}{2^2} - \dfrac{(y-1)^2}{3^2} = 1$

Write the equation for each line below.

23. line A   **24.** line B

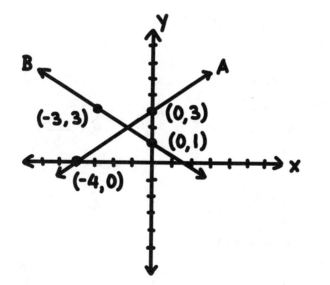

Translate the word problem below into an equation; then solve.

25. The rectangular vegetable garden is 6 feet longer than 2 times its width. If the perimeter is 48 feet, what is the garden's width? (Remember, the perimeter of a rectangle is the sum of all its sides.)

Chapter 14 Test

Tell whether each sentence below is True or False.

1. A group of equations that represent a single problem is called a "system" of equations.

2. No system can ever have two pairs of solutions.

Answer each question below.

3. Tell whether the lines for $y - 3x = -5$ and $y = 3x$ are parallel or perpendicular.

4. Tell the center and vertices of the ellipse for the equation $\dfrac{(x-1)^2}{7^2} + \dfrac{(y-1)^2}{3^2} = 1$.

Factor each expression below.

5. $10x^2y - 5x^3y^2$

6. $a^2 + 2ab + b^2$

Simplify each expression below.

7. $(c-v)^2$

8. $(-2r^3s^5t^2)^4$

9. $\dfrac{a}{ab+b^2} - \dfrac{b}{a^2+ab}$

10. $(x+y)(x^2 + 2xy + y^2)$

Tell whether each pair of expressions below is equivalent.

11. $y^2 - 3by + 2b^2$ and $(y-2b)(y-b)$

12. $9s^2t^4 - 25u^2v^4$ and $(3st^2 + 5uv^2)(3st^2 - 5uv^2)$

Solve each equation below.

13. $\dfrac{1}{x} + \dfrac{7}{5x} = \dfrac{x+2}{x}$

14. $x^2 + 11x = 0$

Answer each question below.

15. In the equation $B = \frac{1}{3}dt^2$, find the value of B when $d = -9$ and $t = 4$.

16. Solve for g in the equation $cdg - eg = ab$, then simplify.

Graph each two-variable equation below.

17. $y = -\frac{2}{5}x + 3$ **18.** $y = x^2 - 4x + 9$

Solve each system of equations below.

19. $\begin{cases} 3x + 2y = -8 \\ -3x + 4y = 20 \end{cases}$ **20.** $\begin{cases} x + 5y = -2 \\ 3x + 5y = -16 \end{cases}$ **21.** $\begin{cases} 2x + 3y = 22 \\ 3x - 4y = -18 \end{cases}$

22. $\begin{cases} 3x - y = 8 \\ y = 2x \end{cases}$ **23.** $\begin{cases} y = 3x \\ y = x^2 + 8x + 6 \end{cases}$ **24.** $\begin{cases} 3x - y + 2z = 15 \\ x + y + z = 4 \\ 2x - 2y + 3z = 21 \end{cases}$

Translate the word problem below into a system of equations; then solve.

25. Tickets to the museum exhibit cost $5.50 for adults and $3 for children. If 110 people attended and the museum sold $487.50 worth of tickets

a.) How many adults attended?
b.) How many children attended?

Chapter 15 Test

Tell whether each sentence below is True or False.

1. When multiplying or dividing an inequality by a negative number, the inequality symbol must be flipped.

2. In a compound inequality, the word "and" means the solutions solve both inequalities, and the word "or" means the solutions solve either of the inequalities.

Simplify each expression below.

3. $(3x^2y^4)(9x^3y^3)(4xy^2)$

4. $\dfrac{2x^3 - 6x^2y + 5xy^2 - y^3}{x - y}$

Tell whether each pair of expressions below is equivalent.

5. $9a^2 - 25b^2$ and $(3a - 5b)^2$

6. $7x^2 + 17x - 12$ and $(7x - 4)(x + 3)$

Solve each equation below.

7. $\dfrac{x}{x-3} - \dfrac{3}{10} = \dfrac{1}{2x-6}$

8. $(x - 5)^2 = -17$

Answer each question below.

9. In the equation $z = \dfrac{x^3 + y^3}{2x}$, find the value of z when $x = -4$ and $y = 2$.

10. Solve for j in the equation $a = \dfrac{j + b}{j - c}$, then simplify.

Write the equation for each line below.

11. Line A   **12.** Line B

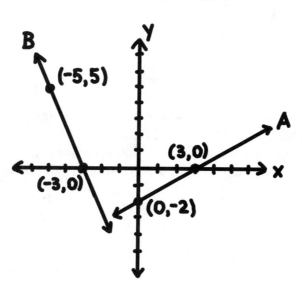

Solve each system of equations below.

13. $\begin{cases} y = \dfrac{1}{2}x \\ 2x - 3y = 5 \end{cases}$

14. $\begin{cases} x^2 + y^2 = 13 \\ y - x^2 = -7 \end{cases}$

15. $\begin{cases} x - 5y + 2z = -15 \\ 2x + 2y - z = 11 \\ x + 3y + 2z = 9 \end{cases}$

Write a compound inequality for each statement below. Also graph each set of solutions on a number line.

16. A quantity x that is greater than -5 and less than 3.

17. A quantity x that is less than or equal to -2 or greater than or equal to 4.

Solve each inequality below.

18. $-3x + 7 \geq 22$ **19.** $3y^2 > 108$ **20.** $-7(x+1) \leq -2(x-5)$

21. $x^2 - 3x - 40 < 0$ **22.** $4x - 8 \leq -16$ or $4x - 8 \geq 4$

Solve each system of inequalities below by graphing.

23. $\begin{cases} y < -2x - 1 \\ y < 2x + 3 \end{cases}$ **24.** $\begin{cases} y \geq 3x - 2 \\ y \leq x \end{cases}$

Translate the word problem below into an inequality; then solve.

25. Mrs. Dundee wants to sell the rights to her new Cajun cookbook and she has two offers. The first publisher has offered to pay $80,000 up front and a $3 royalty for every book sold. The second publisher has offered to pay $30,000 up front and $5 for every book sold. Over what range of sales will Mrs. Dundee make more from the second publisher than from the first?

Chapter 16 Test

Tell whether each sentence below is True or False.

1. One way to understand absolute value is as the difference between two numbers.

2. Another way to understand absolute value is as the positive of whatever quantity is inside the absolute value bars.

Calculate each absolute value below.

3. $\left|-9\right|$

4. $\left|15-10\right|$

Factor each expression below.

5. $4a^2b^2 - 9c^2d^2$

6. $x^2 + 2ax + a^2$

Simplify each expression below.

7. $\dfrac{4}{5}x^3y^4 - \dfrac{1}{5}x^3y^4$

8. $2[3x-(4+5x)]+11x$

9. $\dfrac{\dfrac{y-4}{3(y-1)}}{\dfrac{2y-8}{15}}$

Solve each equation below.

10. $2(x+1)+5x = -17$

11. $\dfrac{1}{x} + \dfrac{2}{5x} = \dfrac{2}{10-5x}$

Answer each question below.

12. In the equation $Q = 0.5an^3$, find the value of Q when $a = 5.2$ and $n = 1.7$. Round your answer to two decimal places (hundredths).

13. Solve for x in the equation $y = \dfrac{z^3}{ax}$, then simplify.

Solve each system of equations below.

14. $\begin{cases} 2x - 4y = -26 \\ 3x - 5y = -31 \end{cases}$

15. $\begin{cases} y = x^2 - 1 \\ y = 3x + 3 \end{cases}$

Solve each inequality below.

16. $2x - 7 > 8(x - 3)$

17. $x^2 + 9x \geq -18$

Solve each system of inequalities below by graphing.

18. $\begin{cases} x + y > 2 \\ y - 2x < -4 \end{cases}$

19. $\begin{cases} y \geq 3x - 4 \\ 2x + y \leq 1 \end{cases}$

Solve each absolute value equation below.

20. $|x - 9| = 23$

21. $|3x + 4| = 11$

22. $\left| \frac{1}{2}x - 13 \right| = -7$

Solve each absolute value inequality below.

23. $|3x - 3| \leq 18$

24. $\left| \frac{1}{4}x + 1 \right| > 2$

Translate the word problem below into a system of equations; then solve.

25. Harrison paid $36.50 for 5 cans of yellow tennis balls and 3 cans of white ones. Beverly paid $50.25 for 7 cans of yellow tennis balls and 4 cans of white ones. If they both paid the same prices,

a.) How much did each can of yellow tennis balls cost?
b.) How much did each can of white tennis balls cost?

$$\left(\sqrt{5x-1}\right)^2 = \left(\sqrt{x}\right)^2 \quad \text{square first}$$

normally

$5x$ solve normally $= x^2$

CHAPTER TEST
ANSWERS

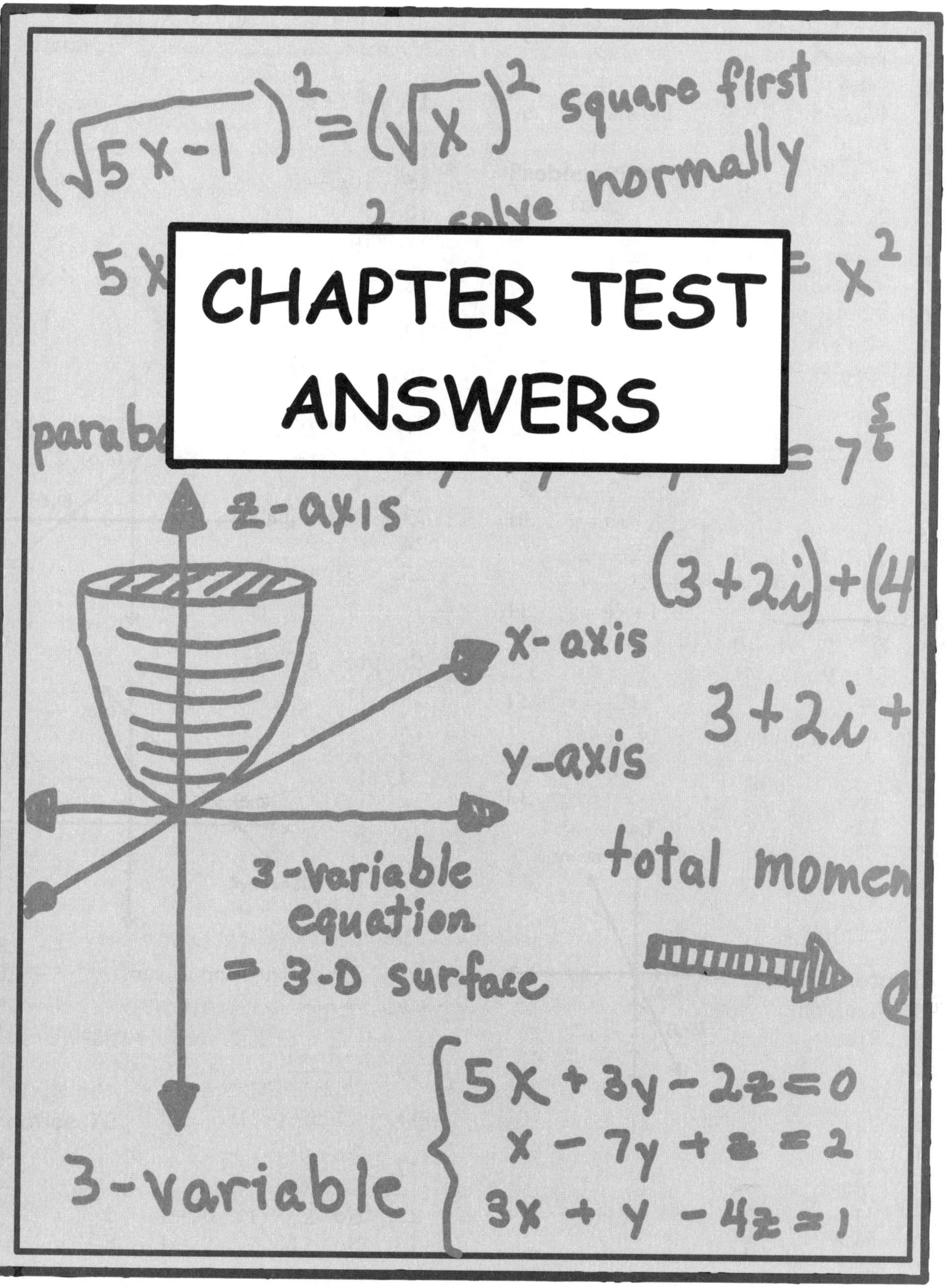

parab $= 7^{\frac{5}{6}}$

z-axis

x-axis

$(3+2i)+(4$

$3+2i+$

y-axis

3-variable
equation
= 3-D surface

total momen

3-variable $\begin{cases} 5x + 3y - 2z = 0 \\ x - 7y + z = 2 \\ 3x + y - 4z = 1 \end{cases}$

Chapter 1 Test

1. True
2. False
3. True
4. B
5. C
6. 25
7. 30
8. -44
9. -37
10. 7
11. $-9(3+6)$
12. $\dfrac{-15}{5} - 8$
13. $\dfrac{x+12}{3} = 20$
14. $4x - 7 = 18$
15. Yes
16. No
17. 22
18. 7
19. 9
20. -102
21. 29
22. $\dfrac{4}{3}$
23. 16.2
24. $\dfrac{11}{6}$
25. $3

Chapter 2 Test

1. True
2. True
3. B
4. C
5. 2
6. 6
7. 33
8. Yes
9. Yes
10. $2.4x$
11. $8x + 3$

12. $\dfrac{3}{5}y$
13. $\dfrac{4}{5}x + 8$
14. $-4x + (-25)$
15. $10x - 40$
16. 7
17. 16
18. $-\dfrac{12}{5}$
19. 2
20. $-\dfrac{2}{3}$
21. Identity
22. $\dfrac{6}{5}$
23. False equation
24. 1
25. $35,000

Chapter 3 Test

1. True
2. False
3. True
4. 14
5. 115
6. 3
7. $\dfrac{4}{3}$
8. $\dfrac{3}{5}$
9. $\dfrac{1}{4x}$
10. $\dfrac{-5x+1}{2x}$
11. $-12x + (-21)$
12. $\dfrac{7x-6}{2x+6}$
13. No
14. No

15. $\dfrac{5}{9}$

16. $\dfrac{55}{8}$

17. $-\dfrac{2}{3}$

18. 3

19. -48

20. $\dfrac{4}{13}$

21. False equation

22. $\dfrac{5}{7}$

23. $-\dfrac{10}{3}$

24. 19 cans

Chapter 4 Test

1. True
2. True
3. True
4. 38
5. -4
6. -147
7. 5.4×10^{9}
8. 2.7×10^{-8}
9. 1.792×10^{12}
10. 1.76×10^{-4}
11. Yes
12. Yes
13. $54x^{15}$
14. $\dfrac{y+3}{y+2}$
15. $x^3 + 8x^2 + 17x + 10$
16. $\dfrac{3x-3}{2x}$
17. $\dfrac{7x+15}{x^2+6x+9}$
18. $\dfrac{-5z^3+1}{2z^2+4z}$

19. 2
20. 4
21. $-\dfrac{19}{5}$
22. $\dfrac{7}{5}$
23. 4
24. $\dfrac{3}{4}$
25. 195 gallons

Chapter 5 Test

1. True
2. True
3. 14,800,000
4. 0.00076
5. Irrational
6. Rational
7. 3.61
8. 4.12
9. $5^{\frac{1}{2}}$
10. $3^{\frac{2}{5}}$
11. $\sqrt{22}$
12. $9\sqrt{3}$
13. $\sqrt[3]{4}$
14. $7^{\frac{5}{6}}$
15. $2^{\frac{3}{10}}$
16. $\dfrac{\sqrt{35}}{7}$
17. $7y^2(3y+2)$
18. $(x-5)(x-4)$
19. $\dfrac{1}{729x^{12}}$
20. $\dfrac{x^2-10x+24}{x^2+3x}$
21. $\dfrac{y+10}{2y^2+6y-20}$
22. 2

23. 23
24. -12
25. 13 hours

Chapter 6 Test
1. False
2. True
3. 1.344×10^{-3}
4. 3×10^{-8}
5. $-7\sqrt{5} + (-13)$
6. $-\dfrac{\sqrt{6} + \sqrt{14}}{4}$
7. $11^{\frac{3}{5}}$
8. $(x-9)(x+4)$
9. $(2x+5)(x+1)$
10. $\dfrac{27}{5x^{14}}$
11. $\dfrac{y}{6}$
12. $\dfrac{x^2+2}{x^2-4x}$
13. Yes
14. No
15. $\dfrac{5}{3}$
16. $+\sqrt{11}, -\sqrt{11}$
17. $4, -14$
18. $0, -4$
19. $7, 3$
20. $\dfrac{5}{2}, -1$
21. $+\sqrt{5}-2, -\sqrt{5}-2$
22. $\dfrac{-5+\sqrt{33}}{4}, \dfrac{-5-\sqrt{33}}{4}$
23. $\dfrac{-7+\sqrt{61}}{6}, \dfrac{-7-\sqrt{61}}{6}$
24. 8, 40

Chapter 7 Test
1. True
2. True
3. $a=4$, $b=2$, $c=-1$
4. $a=3$, $b=-5$, $c=-11$
5. $8\sqrt{3}$
6. $\sqrt{7}$
7. $5^{\frac{7}{12}}$
8. $9x^2(2x+1)$
9. $(x-10)(x+2)$
10. $(2x-3)(x-1)$
11. $\dfrac{20}{z^4}$
12. $\dfrac{3}{x^2-2x}$
13. $\dfrac{3}{x-1}$
14. Yes
15. Yes
16. $-\dfrac{1}{10}$
17. 49
18. 1
19. 6 (3 is extraneous)
20. $-\dfrac{3+\sqrt{7}}{2}, -\dfrac{3-\sqrt{7}}{2}$
21. 16
22. $-7, 5$
23. $\dfrac{-5+\sqrt{65}}{4}, \dfrac{-5-\sqrt{65}}{4}$
24. 93 quarters

Chapter 8 Test
1. True
2. True
3. Real solutions
4. Complex solutions
5. $9i$
6. $2\sqrt{5}i$
7. $4i$

8. $-\sqrt{11}i$

9. $10+12i$

10. $-2\sqrt{3}$

11. $9+8i$

12. 23

13. $-1+17i$

14. $\dfrac{11\sqrt{2}}{2}$

15. $32i$

16. $\dfrac{1}{125y^{21}}$

17. $\dfrac{y-5}{3}$

18. $\dfrac{9x+7}{10x-10}$

19. $\dfrac{1}{2}, 0$

20. $\dfrac{25}{2}$

21. $+\sqrt{29}i, -\sqrt{29}i$

22. $5, -5$

23. $+3i-6, -3i-6$

24. $\dfrac{-3+\sqrt{23}i}{2}, \dfrac{-3-\sqrt{23}i}{2}$

25. 30 degrees

Chapter 9 Test

1. True

2. True

3. 6.74

4. -3.05

5. Complex solutions

6. Real solutions

7. Complex solutions

8. $-6+12i$

9. -27

10. $-26+2i$

11. $(x-3)(x-1)$

12. $(2x+1)(x-7)$

13. $x(x+4)(x+3)$

14. $-4x^5$

15. $\dfrac{1}{6y}$

16. $2x^5-16x^3$

17. $\dfrac{1}{1+3x}$

18. $2x^2+3x+1$

19. $\dfrac{9}{13}$

20. $0, -1, -3$

21. 24

22. $\sqrt{6}, -\sqrt{6}, \sqrt{3}, -\sqrt{3}$

23. $\sqrt{19}i, -\sqrt{19}i$

24. $2, 1, -1$

25. 7 hours

Chapter 10 Test

1. True

2. False

3. 43

4. -12

5. $2x(3x-5)$

6. $(5x-1)(x-2)$

7. $48z^7$

8. $\dfrac{x^2-3x}{2}$

9. x^2+3x-5

10. $-\dfrac{18}{5}$

11. $4, 3, 0$

12. $-4, -5$

13. $y=-2x+6$

x	-2	-1	0	1	2	3
y	10	8	6	4	2	0

14.

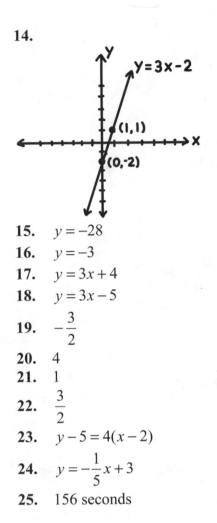

15. $y = -28$

16. $y = -3$

17. $y = 3x + 4$

18. $y = 3x - 5$

19. $-\dfrac{3}{2}$

20. 4

21. 1

22. $\dfrac{3}{2}$

23. $y - 5 = 4(x - 2)$

24. $y = -\dfrac{1}{5}x + 3$

25. 156 seconds

Chapter 11 Test

1. True
2. True
3. Perpendicular
4. Vertical
5. A
6. B
7. vertex $(3, 1)$; opens up
8. center $(-4, 7)$; radius 5
9. $-2x^4$
10. $\dfrac{y^{15}}{27}$
11. $\dfrac{x-5}{2x-3}$
12. $-\dfrac{1}{2}$

13. -6

14. 7

15.

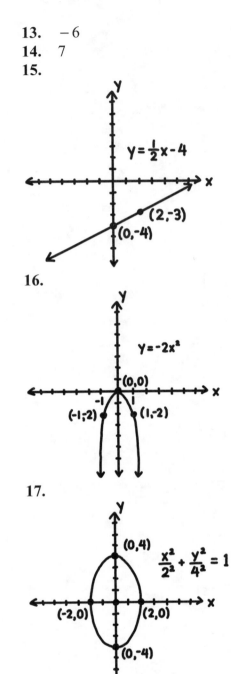

16.

17.

18.

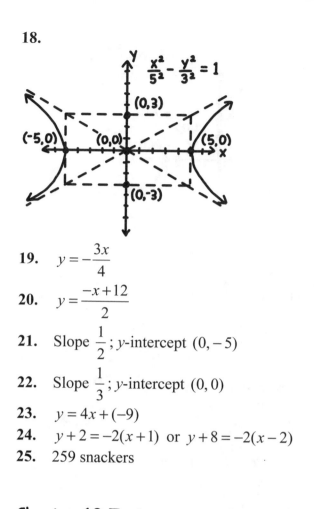

19. $y = -\dfrac{3x}{4}$

20. $y = \dfrac{-x+12}{2}$

21. Slope $\dfrac{1}{2}$; y-intercept $(0, -5)$

22. Slope $\dfrac{1}{3}$; y-intercept $(0, 0)$

23. $y = 4x + (-9)$

24. $y + 2 = -2(x+1)$ or $y + 8 = -2(x-2)$

25. 259 snackers

Chapter 12 Test

1. True

2. False

3. 16

4. $-25 + (-61i)$

5. $\sqrt{74}$

6. Vertex $(-2, 3)$; opens up

7. Center $(0, 0)$; vertices $(4, 0)$, $(-4, 0)$; opens left/right

8. $x^3 + 2x^2 - 11x + 6$

9. $\dfrac{12}{7z^4}$

10. $\dfrac{5x + 4}{20x^2}$

11. $-\dfrac{9}{2}$

12. $8, -5$

13. 4 (1 is extraneous)

14. $f = 3$

15. $u = \dfrac{4Q}{st^2}$

16. $x = \dfrac{b}{a-1}$

17.

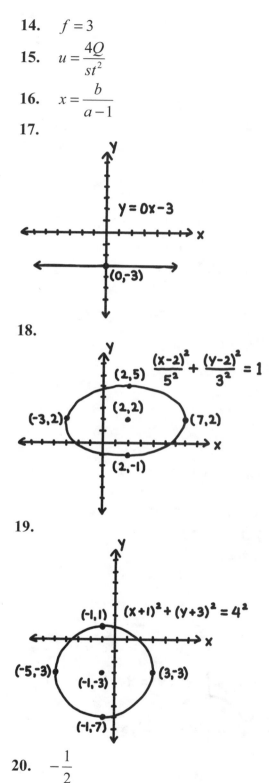

18.

19.

20. $-\dfrac{1}{2}$

21. $y = -\dfrac{1}{5}x + 8$

22. $y - 4 = 3(x-1)$

123

23. $y - 5 = -2(x - 3)$ or $y - 7 = -2(x - 2)$

24. 4 years

Chapter 13 Test

1. True
2. True
3. 5
4. Horizontal
5. Center $(-3, 5)$; radius 8
6. $7a^2bc(ac + 2b^2)$
7. $(x - y)^2$ or $(x - y)(x - y)$
8. $(2s + 5t)(2s - 5t)$
9. $(h + k)(a + b)$
10. $4xy^2z^3$
11. $9f^6g^8h^4$
12. $10s^4t^3 - 2s^6t^3$
13. $\dfrac{x^2 - xy}{bx + by}$
14. $\dfrac{1}{3b}$
15. $2x^2 + 3xy + y^2$
16. -11
17. $+\sqrt{13}i - 6, \ -\sqrt{13}i - 6$
18. 7, 1
19. $y = 21$
20. $q = \dfrac{x - py}{p - 1}$

21.

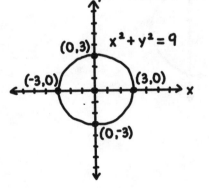

22.

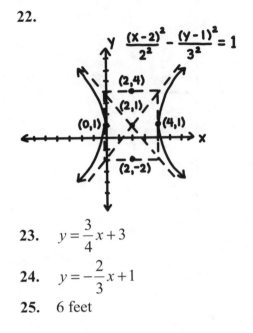

23. $y = \dfrac{3}{4}x + 3$

24. $y = -\dfrac{2}{3}x + 1$

25. 6 feet

Chapter 14 Test

1. True
2. False
3. Parallel
4. Center $(1, 1)$; vertices $(8, 1)$ $(-6, 1)$
5. $5x^2y(2 - xy)$
6. $(a + b)(a + b)$
7. $c^2 - 2cv + v^2$
8. $16r^{12}s^{20}t^8$
9. $\dfrac{a - b}{ab}$
10. $x^3 + 3x^2y + 3xy^2 + y^3$
11. Yes
12. Yes
13. $\dfrac{2}{5}$
14. 0, -11
15. $B = -48$
16. $g = \dfrac{ab}{cd - e}$

17.

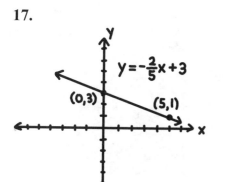

$y = -\frac{2}{5}x + 3$

(0,3) (5,1)

18.

$y = x^2 - 4x + 9$

(1,6) (3,6) (2,5)

19. $x = -4$, $y = 2$
20. $x = -7$, $y = 1$
21. $x = 2$, $y = 6$
22. $x = 8$, $y = 16$
23. $x = -2$, $y = -6$ and $x = -3$, $y = -9$
24. $x = 1$, $y = -2$, $z = 5$
25. a) 63 adults
     b) 47 children

Chapter 15 Test

1. True
2. True
3. $108x^6 y^9$
4. $2x^2 - 4xy + y^2$
5. No
6. Yes
7. $-\frac{4}{7}$
8. $+\sqrt{17}i + 5$, $-\sqrt{17}i + 5$

9. $z = 7$
10. $j = \dfrac{ac + b}{a - 1}$
11. $y = \dfrac{2}{3}x + (-2)$
12. $y - 0 = -\dfrac{5}{2}(x + 3)$ or

$y - 5 = -\dfrac{5}{2}(x + 5)$

13. $x = 10$, $y = 5$
14. $x = 2$, $y = -3$ and $x = -2$, $y = -3$ and $x = 3$, $y = 2$ and $x = -3$, $y = 2$
15. $x = 2$, $y = 3$, $z = -1$
16. $-5 < x < 3$ (or it could also be written: $x > -5$ and $x < 3$)

-5 -4 -3 -2 -1 0 1 2 3 4 5 6

17. $x \leq -2$ or $x \geq 4$

-5 -4 -3 -2 -1 0 1 2 3 4 5 6

18. $x \leq -5$
19. $y < -6$ or $y > 6$
20. $x \geq -\dfrac{17}{5}$
21. $-5 < x < 8$ (or it could also be written: $x > -5$ and $x < 8$)
22. $x \leq -2$ or $x \geq 3$
23.

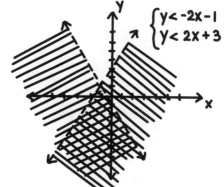

$\begin{cases} y < -2x - 1 \\ y < 2x + 3 \end{cases}$

24.

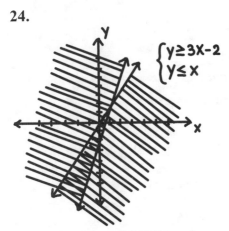

$$\begin{cases} y \geq 3X-2 \\ y \leq X \end{cases}$$

25. More than 25,000 books.

Chapter 16 Test

1. True
2. True
3. 9
4. 5
5. $(2ab+3cd)(2ab-3cd)$
6. $(x+a)^2$
7. $\dfrac{3}{5}x^3 y^4$
8. $7x-8$
9. $\dfrac{5}{2y-2}$
10. $-\dfrac{19}{7}$
11. $\dfrac{14}{9}$
12. $Q=12.77$
13. $x=\dfrac{z^3}{ay}$
14. $x=3$, $y=8$
15. $x=4$, $y=15$ and $x=-1$, $y=0$
16. $x<\dfrac{17}{6}$
17. $x\leq -6$ or $x\geq -3$

18.

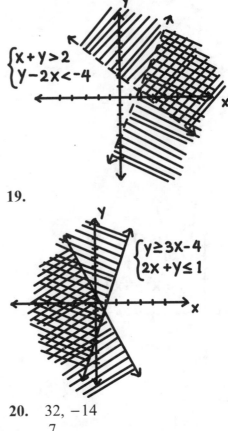

$$\begin{cases} x+y>2 \\ y-2x<-4 \end{cases}$$

19.

$$\begin{cases} y \geq 3x-4 \\ 2x+y \leq 1 \end{cases}$$

20. $32, -14$
21. $\dfrac{7}{3}, -5$
22. No solutions
23. $-5 \leq x \leq 7$ (or it could also be written: $x \geq -5$ and $x \leq 7$)
24. $x<-12$ or $x>4$
25. a) $4.75 for each can of yellow
    b) $4.25 for each can of white